The Cause of Reason

The Cause
of
Reason

Don Smith

Matador
9 Priory Business Park,
Wistow Road, Kibworth Beauchamp,
Leicestershire, LE8 0RX
Tel: 0116 279 2299
Email: books@troubador.co.uk
Web: www.troubador.co.uk/matador
Twitter: @matadorbooks

ISBN 978 1800460 515

British Library Cataloguing in Publication Data.
A catalogue record for this book is available from the British Library.

Printed and bound in Great Britain by 4edge Limited
Typeset in 11pt Minion Proby Troubador Publishing Ltd, Leicester, UK

Matador is an imprint of Troubador Publishing Ltd

ACKNOWLEDGEMENTS

With thanks and gratitude to my editor, Helen Fazal; to Catherine at 2QT for her advice and time; Mungrisdale writer's group for their knowledge and cakes; Angela Locke for her encouragement in the early days; and last, but not least, all the good folk at Troubador for their patience and expertise.

For further reading and information relating to the background and material used in this book, please visit the author's website at: www.concerningreason.co.uk

Creation

Before the seas, and this terrestrial ball,
And Heav'n's high canopy, that covers all,
One was the face of Nature; if a face:
Rather, a rude and indigested mass:
A lifeless lump, unfashion'd, and unfram'd,
Of jarring seeds; and justly Chaos nam'd.
No sun was lighted up, the world to view;
No moon did yet her blunted horns renew:
Nor yet was Earth suspended in the sky,
Nor pois'd did on her own foundations lye:
Nor seas about the shores their arms had thrown;
But earth, and air, and water, were in one.
Thus air was void of light, and earth unstable,
And water's dark abyss unnavigable.
No certain form on any was imprest;
All were confus'd, and each disturb'd the rest.
For hot and cold were in one body fixt;
And soft with hard, and light with heavy mixt.

Ovid, *Metamorphoses*
Book 1: The Creation of the World, 7–24
From a translation by John Dryden

Contents

Preface

E VER SINCE THE MILESIAN philosopher Thales[1] –
and, I imagine, long before that too – humankind
has been gazing into the distance wondering just what
this thing called life is all about: 'What is its meaning?'
'Where do we come from?' 'Why are we here?' And then
that inconceivable question – of whom or what it is that
we are unable to know '… and where did you come from?'

Such a conundrum illustrates the potential for
disappointment in seeking and then finding that final
truth, the truth that requires no further question. It
supposes that we will, in time, become wise enough to
engineer some new form of incarnation thus proving the
present unanswerability of our questions – or, that greater
wisdom will, one day, be revealed to us. If it is the former,
then we shall be the creator of a new destiny. If it is the
latter, then we are not yet ready to acknowledge the folly of
seeking answers to our questions, from ourselves.

---

1   Thales is generally credited as being the earliest known
philosopher, although what little remains of his contribution to
philosophical thinking comes from others who, much later, made
note of his enquiries into principles of physical existence.

But, for the moment, let us ignore the imponderability of time and enjoy the irresistible pleasure of gazing and wondering at the majesty and magnificence of nature. It was, after all, no lesser a mortal than Socrates who said: 'The unexamined life is not worth living.'[2] Considering he was about to be sentenced to death for trumped-up charges against the state, the depth of feeling with which he held this belief can only be imagined. In contrast, St Paul has been interpreted as saying that man's condition must remain entirely hopeless so long as he relies solely upon his powers alone.[3] Similarly, Ibn al-Haytham[4] (Alhazen) in his work *Doubts Concerning Ptolemy* argued that human beings are flawed and that only God is perfect. His faith, like that of St Paul, drove him to question everything that man claimed as emanating from the intellect. In St Paul's case, it was man's interpretation of God's laws that troubled him, whilst Alhazen railed against the quest for truth without acknowledging the 'brilliance of God'.[5]

---

2   According to Plato, said by Socrates at his trial in 399 BCE.

3   *Grace and Law (St Paul, Kant & the Hebrew Prophets)*; Heinz W. Cassier; 1988; p88. This conclusion was reached after Cassier became so disillusioned by Kant's philosophical arguments – what he called 'tyrannical and unreasonable claims made by the intellect' – that he turned to the Pauline Epistles (in their original Greek form; ca. 50–60 CE) to search for the answers he sought.

4   Ibn al-Haytham: 965–1040 CE was a Muslim scholar, engineer, and scientist. Arguably, he was the first person to apply 'experimental' methods to the study of physics and anatomy. His work *Doubts Concerning Ptolemy* was written around 1026 CE and later translated into Latin in the 12th century.

5   Taken to mean that it was God who made man and therefore it was only through God's grace that truth could be known.

Faced with these extremes of belief and doubt in such icons of intellect and reason, is it in any way possible to pursue enlightenment solely through logical or scientific argument? I think not. We need something more.

The question is not so much what or why, but how. How can we reach that point where we are able to say there is more to this than meets the eye: more to this than meets the eye, the brain, the heart – in other words, more to this than meets the condition of being human. To understand, we must first admit defeat to make space for a new consciousness. The intellect is frail, the reasoning is fallible, and therefore the questions are unending. The goal is unattainable: we have no place for that final truth in our present consciousness.

Given such weakness and reluctance to *see*, perhaps it is the journey itself, and not the knowing, that is so fascinating. Were these quests by our forefathers undertaken in the knowledge that they would never reach a satisfactory answer?

If so, then there is, clearly, still a long way to go, and answers – if answers there are – will only come from a distant future far beyond our present understanding. If we think of the time since the creation of the Earth as being just one year, then we have only been looking for just over twenty-three minutes since human life began.[6] However, the concept of time is an irritant interfering with the notion of a more knowing future. If I were to say that there is no reason to think that the future will be any different

---

6   Assuming the Earth is 4.5 billion years old and homo sapiens have been 'gazing' for around 200,000 years.

from the present, then I too would have to believe the quest to be hopeless. However, I refer only to that future which can be imagined by the present condition of life, for we see the future from the constraints of our own time and minds – Humankind, at present, is blinkered by its very humanhood.

Undoubtedly, there will be change; undoubtedly, we will become more knowledgeable, but will we – collectively[7] – know more about Life's place in all about us than did Thales or Socrates, or will we continue to philosophise on the prospect of humankind's ability to conceive of itself? That, surely, is the road we are on by continually asking ourselves such questions.

If the answer lies in the future, then it is a future that at present we may not recognise, a future without time and without the constraining fog of mortality that requires us to believe in no other.

This then is the overarching premise for *The Cause of Reason*: time is an intrusion upon us understanding all that is to be known about life. The answers *are* there, or we would not be here; it is the journey, the discovery, that is the fascination. Such a journey lies both within and beyond mortal tread. To know the fullness of reality

---

7 Collectively, in the sense of a common understanding throughout humankind of the absolute certainty that life is more than can be explained by itself: in a sense, a global consciousness that life is an inferior form of being. For that to come to fruition, it will require evolution of the intellect to know of intelligence (and therefore the possible reason for life) beyond its own boundaries. Collective acceptance in this manner is as necessary to a revolutionary change in human consciousness as was the first use of simple tools by early man.

requires freedom: freedom to think, to believe, and to accept possibilities beyond our present condition.

How we get there is the reward. The story could be anyone's; in fact, it belongs to us all – whatever we believe, we are a part of the future because of what we do in the present. We will become what we are today and what we allow others to be tomorrow.

So, the question is not so much why, but *how* do I come to know? How do I come to know my part in this story called life?

What follows is that quest: humanity's search for peace of mind. It is universal and individual, general and particular; it crosses boundaries whilst remaining motionless in its absoluteness, and it rests within us all. There is nothing remarkable in this, we all have doubts and we all seek greater enlightenment at some point in our lives. But what is unusual about this story is the way it came to be, and to know that we need to go back a very long way indeed: we need to go back to before time itself.

Mary's Story

Awareness

IT IS A STRANGE thing, but ever since I can remember I have thought that others knew my place in this world far better than I do. What I may now think of as a meek-natured, perhaps even submissive, childhood was not at all unusual in a household with three elder brothers. But that is not the beginning of it.

I was born on the tenth day of May in the year 1753, the youngest by some measure and the last that my mother bore. She died not long after.

I recall little of my childhood, a time spent in interminable spells away from home with only an elderly aunt for company. I yearned for it to be different – to spend long days with my father and brothers was my only wish. When, finally, I did return for good (I must have been about eleven or twelve) my father had employed a housekeeper. This I felt was on my behalf and I remember doing all I could to show my readiness to attend to my father's wishes, both in learning and domestic ability. My eagerness to please, I'm afraid, did nothing to smooth the running of the household. She too left us after a short while.

In this way I became my family's keeper. My aunt's tutoring had prepared me for a life of order and routine, and I settled for both with an inner contentment that was reward enough for my labour. I had no desire for more or wish to understand what it was that shaped my world or caused me to wake or sleep within it. In fact, I was so far from concern about anything outside of the four walls that governed my life that I allowed nothing to interfere with my view of it. My life was my world. I had all I needed or expected and that was an end to it.

Except, of course, it wasn't. From knowing little, I came to know the pleasures of love and the need to give more than duty requires: the need to love another for their own sake and not mine. I married and was blessed with a son.

This most certainly was, for me, the beginning. And this explains why I am compelled to share what has become my story. What follows is of such disturbance to my heart and soul that at times words fade as tears fill my eyes. What began as a journal of hope has become a cry for understanding and peace. It has consumed my waking hours, haunted my nights, and spared not a moment of my life since Death twice more crossed my threshold. I claim no answer, only a settlement of mind and at the last a return to that inner quiet of childhood.

The Free Goose

I CAN STILL PICTURE the image of Douglas as he strode across the cobblestones. His nailed boots chattering on ice but never faltering. His figure, centurion-like, wrapped in a flowing cloak, hugged the moon's shadows as he skirted the most uneven undulations. His commanding gait was assured, that much was certain, but the same could not be said for the inner man.

Douglas always focused on the now of his being: he was immune to all possibilities other than that which centred on the beat of his presence. What cannot be addressed, he might have reasoned, cannot be considered as worthy of attention and therefore could have no bearing upon the present. Time, had he chosen to reflect upon it, was his to do whatsoever he wished with. After all, it was free and everlasting.

However, as I now know, what is seen is just the tip of what is, what remains hidden is much more, a fullness of being that lingers as shadows beyond mortal reach to mark the passage of existence forever. In the beginning was Creation: the Word was all things and It begat life.

Now all things have become a servant *to* life. Life has become master without knowing the meaning or reason for it.

Douglas's behaviour was not unusual. He lived without knowledge of his place in this world and without care for anything beyond it. Ignorance, though, has no saviour nor does opportunity care for pity; his was a precarious life lived on a line between competing physical and metaphysical worlds where reality and non-reality come together at a place beyond time to contest for stray souls. Without knowing it, Douglas was a marked man ... it was just a question of time.

The apparent ease of his gait that evening was a sham, an unconscious deception that allowed him to mingle with his adopted kin in a way that avoided attention and conflict. His arrival in the Cumberland valley of Newlands some six years earlier, in the year 1794, was one of those occasions that burns a man and, for better or worse, stays with him as a badge to carry for so long as public memory requires it. In Douglas's case, his accuser's finger was lineage. No one knew his past.

He arrived with travellers for the traditional gathering of rovers and tinkers at the Michaelmas fair and stayed when they moved on. Some say they left him as not being one of their kind, others that he left them to avoid persecution – for what, was never mentioned – but most were agreed that he had a chill about him that was deep-set and hard to ignore in a small community where everyone knew everyone else by ancestry and repute for generations past. That comfort and ease was missing from

6

Douglas's heritage. Whatever the truth of his lineage, he was on the outside and wisely refrained from seeking or accepting close associations with the long-held ways of this rural community. He was content to forego intimacy of behaviour in favour of privacy, and willing to sacrifice the security of station that comes with the common accord of a family line for the freedom to indulge in the pleasures that arise from an independent gaze.

He had chosen the life of a solitary man and had forestalled further reproach by the usefulness of his trade and the strength of his arm. He had the tools, as well as the air, of a blacksmith and had slowly established a reputation as a farrier and wheelwright to the farming community scattered in and around the vale. His work was growing evidence of his presence. In time, it would bear testimony to the durability of his resolve, but for now he was bound to carry the brand of a stranger for as long as he strode amongst the ways of others in this isolated land.

For the moment, though, his journey was short. The cobbles changed to slabs and the slabs to bare floorboards as he stepped into the cosy parlour of the Free Goose Inn. He had been fortunate. Outside, nothing moved – or should I say, nothing that he would have noticed. The time and space that Douglas occupied – or as I have since come to understand, influenced – was full of shadowy activity competing for the right to control and take a place in history. In Douglas's case, the activity was no more or less prolific than usual, but there was an air of persistence that transcended the more recent attachments. The competing legions cannot be counted and no expression of magnitude or effect is appropriate; instead, it is as though a sense of inevitability draws forces of dark and light to a common point in this world. A scent, if you will, one that attracts, sometimes for good and sometimes not. What happens in this competing maelstrom of malevolence and hope has been attributed by some to be luck or fate. I now know that nothing could be further from the truth. Luck has nothing to do with it. There is a force that does not rely on chance to turn the pages of life. Luck is just another word for survival.

Douglas was afforded shelter because of where he was. The Free Goose Inn carried a protective veneer, one that many such places enjoy, without apparent identifiable reason and without any guarantee of continuity. Time, or more correctly that which takes place in the name of time, has many characteristics: some light, some dark, but the most important of all from Douglas's point of view was one of acquired value. The mass of history bears heavily upon the future, and the history of time in the Free Goose Inn was long and benign.

The likeness to any hostelry he had frequented before was remote. The parlour of Freeland, as it was plainly referred to, was not an inn at all, nor was it identified in any way as an inn or as offering anything akin to a free goose. It was simply a parlour, a modest room in a modest dwelling that had once been the site of a modest cowshed.

*

This seemingly playful deception has become to me a

symbol of all that is uncertain in this life. What is to one is not to another; what is plainly seen is not there for all to see, and what we hold as true is as a shadow in the mist of all that we cannot know. We are all unique in the way we see events because we perceive them in time and with the experience of our time. Our life is a singular account of a much richer pageant of all possible eventualities in all possible circumstances.

*

The warmth and familiar scene triggered a pattern of silent greeting and counter-greeting that owed as much to generations of behaviour born from comfort as it did to friendship. He had not disturbed the goodwill of the settled company and for that he was grateful, for it was not their companionship he was seeking. His news would not stir the bowels of those set in the order of routine or rooted in the poverty of desire. Instead, it would be shared with one he had come to judge as of like mind and circumstance to himself – if only in respect of their common signature as newcomers. In the course of their acquaintance it had emerged that the two of them shared an intrigue of the 'wastes', those wild, rarely trodden higher commons and templed crags that were fit only for sheep and foreign miners to seek their chosen pickings. Yes, mutual interest it was, but that was not to say it bound them in all else, for the eye of one is never the same as another.

If some might regard that as friendship, then so be

it. But that would be assuming a degree of reliance upon each other that might not be present in both parties to the arrangement. If relationship there was, then it was as an elder brother to a younger sibling – a relationship of circumstance, no more than that. It was Douglas who had pioneered their expeditions into the hidden quarters of this country, which had been bypassed by shepherds, farmers, and travellers who had sought the attainable heights by more direct, less challenging, less rewarding ways. If this added further to his ostracism then that was his lot. He had no pretence to conformity and no favour with convention. Those who chose his company were entitled to know it and abide by it, rather than to speculate upon friendship or indulge in unfounded discourse upon his independent ways and mind.

Christian rose as he entered. 'How do? I didn't expect thee tonight.' He moved to draw a pot of ale from the oak barrel carefully set between the upturned legs of a discarded milking bench now found on the end of a still-serviceable parlour table.

Fancy change? thought Douglas.

'Mind a change, eh?' continued Christian from his position behind the makeshift bar.

'Just so,' came the involuntary untruth along with the usual halfpenny charge. 'We'll talk later,' he added by way of closure as he moved into the arc of firelight to occupy the vacant table next to William.

The scene was familiar. William's lurcher stretched languidly, close by the open fire, one eye on his master, the other scanning an unmarked but strictly enforced boundary. The smell of wood ash, drying sods, and warm ale mixed uneasily with singed fur, whilst the coarse garb worn by the two-legged assembly slowly released long-forgotten encounters with bog and byre.

George and Joshua sat on the other side of the stone fireplace, oblivious to all but their game. They were watched closely by the 'fath'r', Arthur. Arthur arrived early and rarely left before courtesy to his hosts required him to do so. He drank quietly and never too much. He had, by way of his regular patronage of the Free Goose, a significant influence on the way time acted within the four walls of this makeshift hostelry.

Douglas's arrival had not gone unnoticed by the elderly patrons – unremarked upon, yes, but unnoticed, no. Words were thought of as unnecessary when a glance or sideways movement of the head would do. The cloak that masked his journey to the hostelry was replaced by a lighter wrap of silence. He felt that words were unnecessary, and in the context of where he was and who he was with that night, he was right. He, Christian, and the party gathered around the fire were indeed free men. On this occasion, at least, he was amongst equals.

'Fifteen for two, fifteen for four and eights paired for six.' The slap of card in hand on the oak plank of a tabletop and the knock of a tally block base recorded the imminent closure of one more game on one more day. Like the game and the steaming yarrer by the fire, both players had a finite lifespan, but that would not be reached tonight.

George broke the silence. 'Thou 'ast mere luck than thee's a reet t', Joshua – W'at says thee, Fath'r?'

'Ay … 'appen so.'

The snug was dimly lit. Shadows cast by the light from the fire and the half-dozen or so tallow candles set high on the rough-plastered walls were no barrier to a game of cards or a swill of ale. The flickering light added a sense of exclusivity to the already heavy air of a private club. This was not a place to be seen in, nor was it a place for conversation. It would be going too far to say it was a place to hide in, but it was a shelter from the unknown and ungovernable influences that conspire against life on other occasions and in other places. Time, for once, was on their side.

Time Discordant

THE CONCEPT OF DISCORDANT time – as I shall call it – was unknown to me in those days, but this story cannot be told without mentioning that such a proposition is central, not only to the course of events but to their telling as well.

Time, in the sense of knowing and recalling events in the order in which they occur, does not limit 'being' to a single moment's cameo in which all possibilities, other than that known as life, are to be discounted. Neither does it assume that which is known is the only possible interpretation of the whole event, for that would be to assume a solitary life in which no other took part or held a view. Add to that a life which knows nothing of the concept of time, yet still indulges in its presence through another's view of it, and it can be seen that not only can time be discordant, but it can also be superfluous to all that takes place in its name. Time does not limit life, nor does it play more than a minor part in the greater fullness of existence beyond it. In truth, life has no effect upon time, nor does time record life in any way other than its passing.

There is, I believe, a worldless dimension that encompasses life and all that has been and ever will be, including time. If such a dimension did not exist, then neither would we nor anything else in this timeful universe – for something to be, there must be something else to know of its 'being'. We know what it means to live *in* time by its passing, but what we don't know, and can never know, is what happens *to* time – and for that matter, knowledge *of* time – after humankind ceases to be. That conclusion, that termination of ceaseless questioning, reasoning and knowing, also requires closure, for if not that, then what baseless journey of the soul does life travel?

For the moment, though, it is enough to know that my recording of bygone times takes place from the same world as that in which this story is told – the world with time.

If time can be illusory in what it reveals, then I have found too that words can be equally duplicitous in their conspiracy to deceive in conveying the fullness of all that has to be told. Whether that be through an eagerness to break the silence of unheralded wonders or a dearth of language to convey my story, I cannot say, but at times I confess that words scarcely begin to declare what the mind beholds: the peak of joy, the depth of despair, the pirouette of thought or the leap of heart at a truth found. All such emotions and inner studies studiously shy away from words. It is as though the language of feeling has yet to find a home in something as functional or as general as words on a page.

However, the precision of my account at this moment is secondary to the enormity of the responsibility I have to convey this tale. My unprecedented experience surpasses the use of language. Where I once so casually relied upon words to draw the simplest of pictures, I now have to resort to a sleight of hand that no wordsmith conjurer before has needed to achieve, in order that I may colour the smallest part with the lightest hue, just to suggest the full beauty of what it is that I have to say. Language, I have discovered, is so general, literal, and unforgiving of abuse that at times I must and can only contrive to project the most fleeting sense of wonder by the freeing of the artist's touch across these pages. I ask forgiveness for such allusions as may at times appear too dark to bear, for what is told is beyond all sensible study known to humankind.

The Cause

A MOTHER'S MIND CAN never be at rest until she has the full account for her tribulations. I am not possessed of hindsight, nor do I believe in the right of those who profess a clear line between one occurrence and another. I have, however, come to know that there is a continuation of effect far beyond the intended outcome of a simple choice.

I can only imagine that Douglas's unexpected appearance in The Free Goose that cold January evening was just such a consequence of past elections.

*

Christian moved out from behind the bar towards the table occupied by Douglas. He knew better than to make small talk, but couldn't resist a quizzical: 'Thursday? What's ga'an on?'

Douglas's eye movement was as close an approximation to a smile as was necessary to encourage him to take a seat. There was a lull as he sought to compose his news.

'I've been thinking ...' he began, 'it's time we tackled gully again; weather's right and ...' He didn't need to finish.

'It's reet with me,' assisted Christian, before adding, 'When?'

'Saturday.'

This time it was Christian's turn to pause.

'The First-day ... early.'

The challenge hung between them. Christian was happy with the proposition and Saturday was fine, but it was a joint venture, they each needed the other, and besides he wanted time to prepare himself.

'Sunday it is,' conceded Douglas, 'but we need to ...' He again failed to finish.

'When thee's dun with tattle, lad.'

George had brought the conversation and Douglas's moment to a close.

The gully again, thought Christian, as he moved back behind the bar with George's tankard. This would be the third time that they would set themselves against the top o' dale and the high gully that had so coyly guarded its secrets against their gaze. It had only been by chance that they had first caught sight of its narrow entrance; white and softened by the first snows of winter, it had stood out from the brazen granite rocks shielding its higher reaches. With their fingers, they had followed the line of its scar as far as they could, speculating on what might lie within, until the last slender trace had merged into the protection of the skyline. They had never yet been able to discover its exit; to do that they would have to penetrate its hidden passage. It was this mixture of mystery and modesty, he mused, which had captured their attention and tested their raw skills to new limits of daring. Not that he had much to do with daring. It was Douglas who led and probed when he would have settled for merely being privy to such a secret.

Not that it mattered. There was no choice now that the quest had hold of them. They would go back and back until they had completed it, of that he was sure. He wasn't surprised about the timing either. Douglas had said the weather was right, and so it was. Winter had set in and the temperatures had been below freezing for some time. What snow had fallen would be firm and the route they had taken last time would still be sheltered from the sun. There would be no chance of the wet snow they encountered previously that had forced them to abandon their attempt in acrimony on the final stretch. Yes, this time would see it finished, he thought. He was already mentally preparing himself.

'And wun for Fath'r ... if thee's with us, lad.'

The words drifted into the imagery he had so easily evoked and he smiled to himself as – ridiculously – the picture of George superimposed itself upon his flawed glimpse of the future.

'As I wer' saying,' continued Douglas. 'We need to start before dawn. I'll stop here Saturday.'

'Reet,' was the only possible response.

*

The Free Goose had played host to many travellers in its short history. It would now seem not at all out of place that

Douglas and my son's quest would begin by the crossing of the threshold to leave behind the protective cloak of this unprepossessing hostelry.

Freeland

THE FREE GOOSE HAD been our family's home since
Christian was twelve. I had been left a derelict
smallholding in Newlands – a small, close-knit farming
community just outside of Keswick. This came to me by
way of my father's younger brother, who had never married
and had worked all his life as a stockman for a gentleman
farmer in the Crosthwaite parish of Cumberland. When
his employer died, the land was divided up and sold, but
Uncle William's loyalty had been rewarded with the legacy
of a small parcel of land and a clutch of outbuildings. By
all accounts, he then lived a solitary life. By the time of
his death in the winter of 1787, he had built a habitable
dwelling, gained respect in the community, and established
a presence on the land that founded our family line in the
area.

As his only living relative, the smallholding passed
down to me and my family. However, we did not
immediately take up the opportunity that presented itself.
In fact, it was three years later that circumstance contrived
to leave us with little choice other than to move out of the

Boar Lane district of Leeds and take up residence in the granite building which had once sheltered cattle before providing a home for humans. Freeland, as it became known locally, was once again to become a living part of the community.

Our initial shock at finding ourselves in the country, away from the comfortable surroundings of the town, was nothing compared to Christian's trauma at the shattering of his own familiar world. The loss of his father's job as gangmaster to a team of labourers working on the Otley turnpike, the eviction from our rooms, and our lowering in the social scale meant little to Christian when set against the loss of his friends in the bustling metropolis.

It was not until a full year after my uncle's death that I received the unexpected news of his bequest. A communication – rather formally addressed, I recall, to Mary Elizabeth Newsome – was hand-delivered by a local firm of notaries. It was from a Mr John Parker of Keswick who was acting as Solicitor for the Estates of the Lords of the Honour of Cockermouth. I was thereby advised of my inheritance and customary tenant rights to work the associated pastures in the environs of Newlands, for the right and fitful purpose of the estate, in the manor of Braithwaite and Coledale. I was obliged to make my wishes known for my undertaking at my earliest convenience.

This news came as a great shock. Not so much the fact of my uncle's death, sad though that was, but that he should be in a position to make such a bequest. It was an extraordinary state of affairs to comprehend. I must say that I required further persuasion and assurances from the solicitors that all was indeed in order. Eventually, after much discussion with my husband and the worthy notaries, I was persuaded and formerly duly elected to:

> ... *retain within the bounds of his Lordship's estate the customary rights and responsibilities as most generously bequeathed by William John Rigg deceased ~ and heretofore to the same most generously proffered by the Lords of the Honour of Cockermouth for services most dutifully undertaken to and upon his Lordship's estate ~ both with respect to the aforementioned smallholding in the Parish of Crosthwaite and in the environs of Newlands such retained pastures as herein referred ~ in respect of which said pastures the undersigned person most dutifully and respectfully requests that offer be made for until such time ~ not exceeding three whole years ~ as the undersigned is in person able to fulfil said obligations ~ to whosoever most fit and able to meet his Lordship's wishes ~ and at no gain to the undersigned party ~ the rights herein referred.*

Thus, in the presence of two witnesses, I made my signature to my future intentions. After which, it was explained, it would be countersigned and approved by Notaries Public on behalf of the current Earl of Egremont at the next Court Baron meeting in Cockermouth.

I was to become a lady of property.

The Play

IT WAS A FURTHER year after that when my dear husband had his accident on the turnpike. Following heavy rain, he and a number of men were shoring up an embankment when without warning, they say, it collapsed, killing three and burying six others. He was amongst those buried. Had it not been for the prompt and selfless actions of fellow-workers digging with their bare hands to free the heads of those trapped, I am sure he too would have lost his life.

He spent two weeks in the infirmary before coming home on crutches. It was only then that we learnt that the engineer in charge had blamed him for the collapse and that he had lost his job. The following months were hard for us all as first one and then another layer of social title and respectability were peeled away.

Unable to contest the decision of the engineer in charge, and with diminishing prospects of quickly finding a new position, we had little choice but to avail ourselves of the opportunity to start a new life that had presented itself. I sent word to Mr Parker in Keswick of our intention to take occupancy of the smallholding. In the summer of 1790, after selling what we could to pay debts and buy two sturdy horses, we packed what little we had left into a cart and set out along the Airedale valley to Keighley on the first leg of our journey to Kirkby Kendal.

To call this the beginning of my story would not be strictly correct, for as will become clear there can only be one beginning. However, if a point were to be identified as having a particular bearing upon what was to come, then this would surely be it. Indeed, without this cruel reversal of my family's fortunes, there would be no such story to tell, and who can say to what – or where – that would have led. My husband's accident and my legacy were as opposite poles in a never-ending play of fate and fortune. What may on the surface appear as chance – some fitful parade of disorderly indifference to rule or command – was in truth no less than the unfurling inevitability of change: of play upon play and act upon act that draws the next into line as readily as one thought leads to another or as one breath leads to the next.

It is on such occasions as these that hang the turn of some to make what they will of their lot when they are called to have their say. The cards were cast to lay face down upon the baize to wait disclosure and play against the other. No more the chance to withdraw or fold the hand; cometh the call to lay and stay the best till last, perchance to save the day for one more play.

This was no game. But it was a moment when many plays and turns of change came together to await that call that only later could be seen for what it truly was. No, this was not the beginning, but it was a turn that was to cement my sorry part in its telling, a chronicle unlike any before and one that is unlikely ever to be repeated.

The Journey

O UR JOURNEY WAS LONG. It took the best part of two weeks to reach Keswick. But thanks to the very roads that had taken so much from us, it was achieved without hardship or much lingering reflection on the life we were leaving behind. Indeed, because of my husband's lameness – he still walked with the aid of a single crutch – Christian quickly found he was required to help with the regular changeover of Baron and Lord, our two Cleveland Bay horses, that we were told would pull all day long on road or farm if fed and watered well. Christian made it his job to do both and was soon calling for frequent stops for water or roadside grazing for the pair. He learnt quickly and showed a caring nature for their welfare, which we noted with pleasure and relief.

We had been concerned about the effect such an upheaval would have on our son, and now, whilst the boyish exuberance was stilled, we were seeing the first signs of maturity and thoughtfulness as he adapted to his new circumstances. He had become a companion to the family's need, and the journey became a time for exchanging plans and probing our hopes and fears for the future.

It may have been something to do with the nature of the slow, uneventful procession, dictated as it was by the steady rhythmic step of the horses; it may have been the fine weather, fresh air and lengthening summer days; it may have been a release from the mounting prospect of eviction from our lodgings in Leeds and the likelihood of the downward spiral into dependence upon alms or worse, or it may even have been just the anticipation of a fresh start; but whatever the cause, the simplicity of our situation, together with all our possessions in one cart, seemed to be conducive to lengthy story-telling and good communion. My husband, in particular, told the tales that Christian loved: of the English and Scots fighting battles outside Leeds and how, when he was young, he and his family had had to flee the town for their lives. He spoke of life before the roads, before the coming of the stagecoach and oil lamps in the streets of the town, as though it was all there, still, in front of him. As for myself, when not engaged with my journal, I did what I could to tell of the markets, the wool and cloth merchants, the building of the infirmary and the coming of the traders to Leeds. But I could not compete with my husband's stories about the roads: the roads that gave people who had never left their villages the chance to go to the towns and hear the news and watch the hangings of highwaymen who had robbed the rich as they travelled in their finery by stagecoach.

These stories came alive as we approached each new turn in the road, each hushed dell, or each concealing brow as being just the sort of place a determined highwayman might lie in wait for his next victim. We watched as Christian kept a lookout for the glint of sunlight on a raised pistol, or the giveaway outline of a highwayman's billowing cloak against the lighter colours of summer on the rolling countryside. He certainly had his father's eye for detail.

And then there was the stagecoach – was there ever such a sight in all the world? It came as we neared to make our early morning approach into Kirkby Kendal. The nature of the road and the lie of the open country had changed from the rural, dewy-shades of pastoral dawn to the more urban damp-greys of the industrial time-clock. We became increasingly embroiled in the hustle and bustle of carriages, as packhorses and carts made way for larger carrier-wagons, stacked high with bales of cloth and bulging sacks, as they sought their unsteady exit from the town on their journey south. The smell of leather mixed with horse sweat and snuff vied for our attention with the shouts of wagoners as they tried to clear the way for their straining mounts. Our two horses became skittish and shied against the growing melee and unfamiliar mixture of swirling dirt and noise. In all this, I can still feel the growing sense of tension and unease at this sudden change in pace and occupation of the road.

As we reached the outskirts of town, the confusion was further compounded by the cacophony of the sounds made by livestock being driven to market, and the calls of the persistent pedlars seizing the opportunity to sell their wares to the stranded travellers. Then, as though a peak of chaos had been reached and no more could be tolerated, through all this commotion of commerce, turmoil of labour and hazed spectacle of dusty industry, there came the muffled call of a horn that built to a crescendo of crazed trumpeting, as the most magnificent stagecoach ever seen parted the heaving mass. Six rearing, snorting, fire-blowing – as they seemed to me – earth-beating horses, darkened the skies as they bore down upon us and our tiny cart. With a cry of alarm, my husband drove hard off the road. The stagecoach driver's whip cracked above the leading pair to wheel the thundering Flying Machine around our hindrance. The driver swore at the howls of protest from his ruffled passengers. Then, as I recall it, looking straight down at me, he beamed the grin of a man who revelled in his eyrie-like dominance from peer rebuke, before once more wrestling his winged chargers and squealing payload back into the scattering fray on the turnpike. The moment passed. As the dust settled and the tiered travellers faded from view, we eased our way back into the closing ranks of the more grounded – albeit equally dishevelled – stream of humanity flowing the opposite way into town.

The contrast with the isolation of the small communities, rolling dales, and moors we had so leisurely made our way through the past few days could not have been greater. The fragrant pastures were replaced by fetid enclosures of industry. The wide country vistas were foreshortened by the steepling proximity of workhouses and municipal edifices. The expanse of our communion had changed, too, so that we drew closer together in the silence of strangers amongst the neighbourly hubbub of townsfolk and kindred parishioners. The scene was not altogether different from what we were used to in Leeds, it was just that circumstances had changed; we were now detached from the familiarity of association that comes with local custom and heritage. I shall always remember that curious feeling of aloneness amongst so many.

We stopped long enough to replenish our provisions and buy feed for the horses and some very favourably priced wool before, in early afternoon, we headed north and away from the town on the road to Keswick.

As we wound our way through the grey streets back onto the turnpike, our spirits lifted. Soon we were eagerly seeking sight of the mountains that we had been warned would darken our journey by casting a woeful shadow over the sun by mid-afternoon. Every fell was closely scrutinised for signs of the 'terrible dark cloaks' that were prone to 'swirl and descend to envelop all in their path'. However, no such fate overtook us and we reached Winander Mere without mishap.

That evening as I lay under the stars listening to the lapping of the water on the stony shore and the hushed sounds of my family sleeping, I was certain that I heard in some distant land the crack of a stagecoach driver's whip urging his flying team down the dusty turnpike and on through the night to the faraway silhouette of London town.

*

It is from such trespass of waking hours upon the sandman's time-clock of sleep, that dreams will seek to span the gulf between what is seen and what is held – so deep – within as to taunt the foolish mind until – once more – it can find again the comfort of the day's respite.

What is it that bridges light from dark to give sight of shadows lost in day's clear eye the chance to walk again across night's misty mirror to put right some wrong – or misconceived – notion of future prospect, not yet plain enough for mortal sense to grasp?

*

No sooner had the night stolen the last of the day's images and sounds from my mind than I was aroused by the gentle touch of my husband's hand on my shoulder. Just as had been foretold, I found myself enveloped in a cloak, only this was white, wet and stealthily silent. This was indeed a strange place: a mysterious world of dreams and clouds that made people disappear, only to be restored as breathless words and shrouded images to tell of things unknown and hard to place in any waking hour yet come. Such embracing warmth was companion to a sleeping heart, but brought a fearful chill to the cock-crow mind as life took hold once more to sweep aside night's fanciful imagery.

We stayed ever close together as we prepared for the new day.

The road ahead lay tight to the lake. We saw little about us until we came to the Ambleside turnpike where four figures were gathered secretly in the mist talking to the gatekeeper and his wife. Much to our concern, we learnt that just the evening before, a lone highwayman had held up a gentleman-farmer by name of John Rainscombe. He was from Bowness, some three miles south of the hamlet, and therefore close to where we had spent the night. The highwayman robbed him of money and a horse before fleeing across the fells in the direction of Kirby Kendal. A shot had been fired and, although no one had been hit, Mr Rainscombe had later sent riders to Keswick and Kirby Kendal to alert the constables.

It was felt by all that it would be unwise to travel further alone, and as the gatekeeper assured us that we could still reach Keswick by nightfall – so long as we left before noon – we elected to wait and see what other carriage would be upon the road that morning before setting off again.

*

My dream, it seemed, had been what I wanted it to be: a lightful eye too shy by far to inspect the whispering entrails of sleep. Once more I stood condemned, deceived by my belief in my unfailing rightfulness. I said nothing about what I may or may not have heard the night before.

*

As each new traveller joined the party, so our story was told afresh. Our family's business and recounting the journey from Leeds was much in demand, especially when my husband embellished the tale with a few anecdotes of his work building the very same roads we had travelled. He was, I noted, less inclined to mention the incident with the Flying Machine, although, after one or two quiet reminders that also became a part of the story.

As for me, I was engaged in exchanging news with the growing number of womenfolk who, sensing the opportunity for some impromptu trade of hastily made fire-cakes, had by now gathered in readiness for each new arrival joining the queue. I learnt that Uncle William had been well known in the area, both for his expertise as a stockman and as a fierce competitor in the local wrestling tournaments. I was pleased by this news. We exchanged invitations, and introductions were extended to relatives and acquaintances in the settlements that lay ahead on the road to Keswick.

Within a short time, a community of wagons, packhorses, and local farm traffic had mustered in good humour in front of the gatekeeper's cottage. Around mid-morning, as the sun dispersed the last of the mist, we led off the emboldened party to much waving, barking of dogs, and good wishes for a safe journey. When all was said and done, this had been a fortuitous delay, for not only had acquaintances been made, but word would spread along the road and I could see that our credentials would be aided by association with an event of such local noteworthiness.

The road to Keswick was indeed good. The recent fine weather had hardened the surface so that the many small rills and becks that in winter would have threatened our passage were now easily accommodated by the distinctive stone bridges and channels engineered by its builders. The imposing scenery dominated the eye and there was no shortage of finger-pointing or name-calling to witness a new feature or change of light upon some expanding vista. Within the hour we approached the village of Grasmere nestling comfortably in the sunlight below Helme Crag.

The dark-greys of cathedral peaks and buttresses surrounding the lake were beautifully complemented by the more regular lines of whitened walls and slate roofs of the small cottages. Dark-green firs and yews casually mixed with the lighter shades of the English oak in a vision of rural harmony and tranquillity.

The party was bound to stop to exchange news. We took great care in passing on all the salutations entrusted to us before striking out on the winding incline up Dunmail Raise. On the advice of the wagoners, Christian harnessed the second horse in line to share the load. Whilst my husband led the pair up the rise, Christian and I carried the wooden shoes in readiness to place under the cart's wheels to arrest any backward slide. There were frequent shouts of encouragement to the straining horses as we wove our way between the boulder-strewn flanks closing in upon our progress.

The quilted stone walls stitched together the contours of this unruly land: grey and dark seams, a medley of rank and rubble, perching limpet-like defending some ancient honour – now so close as to smother all light, now so distant as to expose all terrors – first sheltering then revealing the stretched line of travellers to the unceasing stare of the shadowy gargoyles leering down upon us. It was just a matter of time, I thought, before they would stir to unleash more blackened bolts into our path. I joined Christian in haranguing the toiling beasts as he put his shoulder to the rear of the cart. I had no wish to tempt whatever it was these sentinels were guarding out of its slumber.

Miraculously, we reached the Raise without mishap to be greeted by two men on horseback: a constable from Keswick and a parson. I was not at all surprised to see the parson. How else were we to pass through this lair, if not protected by his preaching? Sadly, it transpired that he was bound for Grasmere, and as the constable had reached the limit of his jurisdiction – Dunmail Raise marking the boundary between Westmorland and Cumberland – he would commence his descent without further delay. The constable was to accompany our party on the road to Keswick.

After a short break to water the horses, and as the heavier wagons started to top the Raise, the constable led us off across a lighter patchwork plateau of grazing and open moor before reaching the descent to Wythburn Water.

The unobstructed view through the valley ahead to the fading blue of distant peaks foreshortened the drop into the darker greens of the wooded shoreline before us. My first thoughts were that Cumberland looked very much like Westmorland, but with bigger and greater number of mountains. In every direction, as far as I could see, these too were now closing in upon us; those that were not, I judged, were merely waiting their turn to do so.

The road was no less tortuous than that coming up, and having again tethered one horse to the rear of the cart, Christian and I were now charged with arresting the pace of descent by walking behind and pulling on ropes attached to the side of the cart. To tell the truth, I was smitten with these new surroundings. I recall frequently urging Christian to gaze upon some silver rivulet fleeing the mountainside or to look at the sheep patrolling back and forth across the lower slopes in search of sweeter grazing. When not engaged in the scenery or acknowledging the waves from women and children along the way, I resolved to take to this new way of life by numerous well-intentioned undertakings: the keeping of poultry, growing of vegetables, the spinning of yarn, and schooling for my son. My enthusiasm must have been infectious, for as we approached the water's edge, the straight-backed constable, who in comparison was a man of few words, read with great assurance from the immutable lettering on a weathered encrusted milestone:

'Keswick – eight miles!'

This stern and irrefutable pronouncement was much in keeping with the presence of the mountains about us. As we traversed the lakeside boundary, there was no escaping the feeling that Mother Nature was channelling both the endeavours and progress of man and, although entrancing, that this place could frustrate and torment anyone who tried to tame it. The enclosures of young oak and beech struggling to take root on the uninhabitable slopes encapsulated the effort required to make a mark on this land.

After some two or three miles of casual progress, we came across several men engaged upon repair to a narrow crossing of the water. The constable pointed out that it could be used as an alternative route to Keswick, but only by those on horseback familiar with the track through the hills. My husband was particularly taken with the construction of narrow bridges and partly submerged causeways, which we were told had been the only way out of the valley before the road was built. Even now it was still in demand by those who wished to avoid the payment of tolls on the turnpike, encouraged, it would seem, by the local Lord of the Manor, who still funded the upkeep of the crossing. However, as this was not an option for us, we soon regained the road and started to draw away from the water on the final stage of our journey, passing the said lord's manor house as we did so.

In less than three hours we crested the last rise of the day above Keswick. Here we witnessed the light of the lowering sun leaving the ruffled lines of Derwent Water before settling behind the fells that were to be the backdrop to our new life. We took our leave of the constable, and as the last of the wagons rolled past, the three of us made our way around the outskirts of the town and down to the lakeside. We had resolved to begin our new life on a new day.

Home

OUR INTRODUCTION TO KESWICK the following morning was much unlike our entrance to Kirby Kendal. The town was quieter: the sense of drowsy decline – albeit with an air of pastoral occasion to its sleepiness, as though waiting for a call to rise from its slumbers before showing its true colours – contrasted with our alertness as we inspected each silent doorway and still aspect offered. The main street was characterised by a series of cobbled ways leading to, what appeared to be, abandoned works or closed premises associated with mining or forging of some kind. But there was a goodly market square and an imposing central hall of some stature. The shops were well stocked and a few early traders were beginning to offer their wares from open wagons.

Mr Parker was as comfortable in his manner as the town was content in its environs. His welcome was subdued, but sincere. Without flourish or unnecessary ado, he portrayed an air of distinguished solemnity that matched both the occasion and setting. After establishing the rights and admission fines for land to be managed in connection with the smallholding, we became the proud new owners of Freeland. As joint customary tenants of small parcels of land, we were obliged to maintain pasture for the grazing of sheep and cattle as directed by tenant farmer Joseph Bowes of Braithwaite. We were to improve and maintain near fifteen acres in total. In return, we would be allowed to husband such additional beasts as the land and common grazing would sustain without detriment to the farmer's requirements. We would also be required to perform other duties, such as ploughing and harvesting, as required by the farmer. The dwelling itself was ours and would pass down through the family line; however, should we choose to sell, the lord's estate retained first rights to repurchase.

Having satisfactorily settled business matters, we set about securing all necessary and immediate provisions. Salt, flour, cheese, oats, and mutton were easily obtained along with a cockerel and hens that I was assured would be well suited to the needs of both pot and yard. There was no reason for further delay. With a mixture of excitement and apprehension we set out westwards from the town until, crossing the bridge over the Greta River, we were finally alone with our thoughts. This land now held our future and would not release us easily. I distinctly remember the fussing of the hens as they sought their freedom from the loose-woven sack in the back of the cart.

As directed by Mr Parker, soon after crossing the Derwent River we turned south to the small hamlet of Stair, which in his words, 'would present itself as pleasant a gateway to your future as any nestling group of comfortable dwellings could'. Certainly, it looked welcoming, and as we paused to make our business known, it proved to be so, for William Rigg was well thought of in these parts. My growing affection for my late uncle was not misplaced as I learnt more about his life in the valley's farming community.

The road by now had become more of a track, and as we followed the rutted rise away from Stair, the full magnificent expanse of Skiddaw and Saddle Back was laid out behind us. It was as a backdrop to the generously numbered pockets of woodland and fertile plain, now gradually channelling our path into the narrower confines of the valley ahead. Cattle and sheep grazed on the fellsides above the uncut fields of oats and newly scythed pastures with their small stacks of hay peppering the trim grasses. The fragrance of summer and the never-ceasing washing of water over errant rocks and fractured earth was to be with us the rest of the way to our destination at the head of the valley. Our laden cart was led twisting and wrestling its way over and around the intruding roots of gnarled, weather-bent trees and unyielding stones, which marked the limit of men's ability to create inroads into this landscape. All the time rising before and alongside us were mountains of all shapes and form, appearing and fading from view as another turn or enclosed woodland momentarily shielded our gaze, only to as quickly again free our inquisitive inspection with a new vista surpassing the last and drawing us further into this intoxicating spell of noble beauty. It was as though, one after the other, these imperial statues were vying for our attention, like peacocks preening their glory in some royal garden of emerald perfection.

We passed a few scattered dwellings, some hard by the track, others set back with a gate or wall to mark a boundary one from the other. At each, as the opportunity presented itself, we called out to announce our business and seek the names of our neighbours. In all we did this some ten or more times. In turn, we were warmly welcomed with advice and directions for acquiring what we might need to make our home in the valley. We were told the best source for timber and stone for building, for good water, and fuel for the fire, for common grazing and casual labour, and best of all, I remember, from Christian's point of view, was the interest shown in our two horses. My husband had bought wisely; their strength and undoubted good condition, after all the careful grooming from Christian along the way, attracted much admiration and offers of work. Our son, God bless him, was so pleased with all the attention they drew.

There was one final descent, one more bridge, one last turn, till we saw before us the remaining few buildings in the valley, the first of which I knew from the description given to us was to be our new home. We stopped: a small family party of man, woman, child, beast, and fowl gazing in silence at our future.

To describe it as modest would be to exaggerate its status, but its appeal as a shelter in keeping with its surrounds was without doubt. The stone walls were without wash, but had been carefully set to encompass a natural low outcrop of rock at one corner, before stepping away in angular order of size and boldness of shape to a shuttered window and recessed doorway. The effect was mirrored on the other side to give a pleasing symmetry of appearance. On the far end was a small yard that extended in front of the house to the boundary of the track, thus providing a ready entrance for beast and means of escape for fowl. Halfway down the side of the house and extending the full width of the yard was a largely open-faced stone building that had, judging by the number of stalls within it, been used to provide winter shelter for stock, and could now easily accommodate horses and strolling chickens aplenty.

Alas, all this as real as it seemed to be was too readily assimilated by wishful gaze and unchecked imagination. Upon a second and more careful inspection, our regard for reality would surely have queried the gaping holes in the roof and questioned the place of the twisted tree taking root inside the house, its withered arms reaching for light through the front door. If not this, then how was it to be that beast and fowl would wander freely in the yard atop the stone and timber that lay there in great store waiting to be returned to its rightful place in the walls and on the roofs?

And there was more. Covered as it was with the debris of vacant neglect, the yard had been slow to give up its decaying rebuttal of our rash appraisal. The putrid underbelly of winter's animal shelter, stirred as it had been by the summer sun, now reached out with such an air of pungent intrusion upon our lingering inspection as to blanch the strongest sense of uncritical approbation.

My senses swooned under the manure-rich odour of percolated urine and byre dung. My lungs groaned for breath free of the prickly briar of deleterious inhalations, and my eyes watered for want of ventilation. But all this was to evaporate in the throes of a greater will to belong. It was a mere distraction to its potential. At this sighting, it was indeed near derelict and would require a good deal of work before being fit for habitation, and then some more before it could be called a home. But, in truth, it was as appealing then as it is now: a lordly residence in all respects.

I remember my husband's words as though it were yesterday: 'It is a fine building in a fine setting. I feel a kinship about us that tells me we shall prosper here – of that I am sure.' With that he led us in prayer and gratitude for a safe journey before we crossed the threshold of our new home to begin our labours.

A New Life

THERE WAS NO PLAN, no vision, and as it turned out, no choice. As my husband frequently said in those early days: 'It is God's will and His country, and we are bound to both.' It was a simple approach; recognition that life deals a hand that you must live by without wishing for more. Slowly, we re-established our lives to the point where our home had once again become part of the community.

We exchanged labour for such necessities as we could not buy. I added geese to my growing number of hens, and we acquired two mangy dogs that soon found their place in the yard's social order.

Christian's transition to country boy, it must be said, was slower. He was suspicious of his peers and cautious in showing his advanced learning. He was, though, inquisitive. When not 'helping out on the farm', as he called it, or tending the horses, he was a great explorer of the valley with its secluded ways and hidden corners. He took to journeying further afield into the higher reaches to discover the hidden nooks on the slopes of those idle mountains.

What had first appeared as one great valley was, he assured us, rather a series of smaller sheltered vales, each offering its unique perspective of the day and its superior sovereign. The whole now seemed as though some great hand had rested for a moment in the clay of creation to leave a series of slender finger and thumb-like imprints on the landscape before clawing its way out over the valley tops to continue its work. It was here, in this skeletal-scouring, that he found the abandoned spoils from old copper and lead mines; those same dungeons, first hewn from the belly of these hills by miners two centuries earlier, now provided rich seams for his imagination as he searched for undiscovered treasures.

The few miners who still worked in the one remaining open mine lived a frugal life in what was no more than a series of dilapidated huts close to the mine's entrance. Some, it was said, chose to live in the mine itself; either way, it was a much reduced operation from that which it had once been. Occasionally, one or two of them would call at Freeland to buy poultry or milk, as could be spared, to supplement what meagre rations were provided by the weekly packhorses from Keswick. Otherwise, they kept themselves to themselves. They did not take to mixing with the local community. Indeed, they would often be sent away empty-handed from other houses, but that was not my nature; they had shared their lives with Christian and did not prevent him from his explorations around the mines. It was the least I could do.

It was no coincidence that Christian was inclined to be cautious about his new surroundings. None of us were there by choice and the tendency was to withdraw into the comfort of the family. This was an instinct that protected all the community from the potential threat of strangers. In time, the evidence of our hard work in restoring Freeland earned respect, drawing us closer to the people and lifestyle of those around us.

The daily routine was one of industry and willing sacrifice for an undefined greater good. We lacked the occupying sense of security or anonymity that was part of life in a town; the rural community in which we now found ourselves, offered neither of these veneers. We could not find safety in numbers nor hide in a crowd. Acceptance in a small group comes from witness and evidence, not from the metropolitan self-esteem and hearsay we were used to. The convenient façade of behavioural casting found in the urban social-class system has no place in small populations where the wealthiest is dependent on the humblest, not only for services provided but also for respect and protection. This mutually benevolent dance is a necessity that reflects the social health of any group or community that coexists together. This was a lesson long in learning.

There was a sense of creation in forging a way of life that was hard but rewarding. The working day was governed by the needs of the cattle, sheep, and fowl that helped to sustain us, as well, it must be said, as a growing number of our less fortunate neighbours. When not tending to the animals, my husband and Christian would use the horses to fulfil their duties to the farmer by ploughing new land or harvesting crops. Only then, when all else was done, would we be able to turn to work on the house or outbuildings. We laboured long hours to collect rough stone from the wastes and our allowance of timber from the manorial woods. My husband would sell or exchange what hay or straw he could spare from the leased meadowland, whilst I would offer board to passing Johnny Whipcat pedlars in exchange for cloth or other wares from their carts.

Christian helped his father in any way he could, often by herding the few sheep and cattle we had bought in the early days from the proceeds of our labour. It had been the income from work with the horses that had enabled us to purchase twenty Herdwick ewes and two Longhorn cows for eight guineas from a sale of stock over Braithwaite way. My husband had agreed with the farmer to lease two small closures near to us, and the sheep were to graze on the lower hills in the summer months, and we were advised that if we managed the rotation carefully, the closures would yield enough grass and hay for winter feed for the horses and cows, as well as providing winter quarters for the sheep. This had been Christian's first experience of gathering sheep, and even with the help of our neighbour the journey back had taken far longer than expected; they didn't arrive home until well after dusk. The noise of the sheep in the yard and the commotion caused by the geese at being temporarily ousted from their chosen quarters meant that nobody got any sleep that night; the marking and release of our small flock onto the hills was a priority for the next morning.

*

All this: this change to new ways, fresh thoughts and uncertain ends was, I now see, a charge upon each one of us to renew our view of what it was that turned such a rough and ready mass into a place that had at first beckoned and then held our attention in its unfashioned and unframed hand.

*

Amongst all the toil and hardship there were those times that everyone looked forward to. Lambing brought the whole community together, and the birth of a calf or two could make the difference between coming home from market with much-needed provisions or having to go without until harvest time brought another opportunity to replenish a dwindling larder. There were fairs, too: Lent, Easter, Whitsuntide, Michaelmas, Christmas; all had their place in the rural calendar. Such occasions would mean a day out for all the family to Keswick or Cockermouth, to socialise and show off in the company of neighbours, not only from Newlands, but the adjoining valleys of Borrowdale, Bassenthwaite, and Buttermere as well.

But without doubt it was the Newlands Michaelmas fair that was most looked forward to. It was the valley's chance to celebrate harvest and display its wares amidst the splendour of the fading colours of the first days of autumn. It was a setting as fine as could be found anywhere in the county and our family was as bold as any in praise for its superiority to all other. As well as a day for the trading of livestock, this was also a time for the selling of garments made from the valley's own fleeces. Many of the families who had produced rough homespun garments for generations came well prepared with winter shawls, coarse woollen jackets, and waistcoats to sell. It was a timely reminder that the late September sun was the herald of colder days, as the lengthening shadows threw their cloaks across the day's festivities.

It was in 1794 that my husband bought one of my most treasured possessions from the fair. Amongst the many makeshift displays at the show was one by miners selling blue crystals, which they had fashioned into brooches and attractive pendants. I was particularly smitten with a decorative piece left unframed in rock and was delighted, whereupon finding it too expensive to buy, to be offered it at a fraction of its asking price as a token of their appreciation for what we had done for them. There were games aplenty, too, with tug-a-war and wrestling for the men, and stilt races, running and throwing sports for the children, and dancing for all. Much to Christian's surprise, I think, my husband and I were roundly applauded for our part in a spirited reel.

It was at this fair that Christian first met Douglas. He was one of a band of travellers who were selling an assortment of household wares – there were pots and pans, cloth, dyes, and dressmaking materials, and they had also brought tins of exotic spices and foodstuffs not seen in the valley before. As the final day wore on, some of the travellers gathered together in small groups to provide strolling musical entertainment, whilst others set about encouraging fairgoers to an open-air play. As I recall, there were a few bawdy sketches about King George and his courtiers, but the main attraction was a re-enactment of a battle fought by the Royal Navy against the French on the high seas.

I am sure that it was this more boisterous spectacle that caught Christian's attention, especially when a wagon masquerading as a ship of the realm drew up behind the makeshift stage to fire a broadside of gunpowder that startled everyone before covering the cheering throng with smoke and the stench of sulphur. It was Douglas, Christian discovered later, who had set off the gunpowder and then used firecrackers to replicate the sound of musket fire as the troops leapt from the gunship onto the stage to overpower the French sailors and rescue the captured maidens. All this was accompanied by the mock incredulity of the blackened-faced storyteller and cheering crowd.

This was not the first time that Christian had heard the sound of gunpowder. He was accustomed to the muffled explosions coming from the mines, but he had never seen or heard them close to. So it was that when the play was over he took the opportunity to venture behind the stage to see for himself the source of all this wizardry. It was here that he found Douglas. In amongst all the bustle and clamour of the groggy cast, he first formed the impression of a swarthy man who had gunpowder ingrained into the already sun-darkened hands and face of someone used to labour and exposure to extremes of weather. His breeches, although for the most part covered by an old and heavily stained leather apron, were ingrained with the singes of many – far too many for anyone who knew what they were doing – encounters with untamed explosions and unforeseen flashes of fireworks. He seemed to relish his work, for he was surrounded by an impressive array of crucible-like metal bowls, cylinders and heavy hooped kegs, which judging by the many visible scorch marks were also prone to the imprecision of his art.

Christian had been about to retreat in the face of all this evident indifference to care when Douglas had beckoned him to stay and had even seemed to welcome his boyish excitement at the apparent danger of the proceedings. He showed Christian the tools of his trade as a blacksmith and offered his services as a farrier when Christian mentioned our two horses. He had thought Douglas older than himself, perhaps twenty or more years of age, and stronger, yes. But, as it was his first visit to the valley, he deduced that Douglas had not been with his fellow travellers for long. He suggested that if Douglas should care to make his way further along the track to Freeland, he would point out some of the abandoned mines and what was left of their assorted rails and the twisted ironwork that littered the once busy workings. Douglas had said that he would indeed be interested. They parted as the events of the day drew to a close and those with a distance to go set out on the return journey, still singing their allegiances to King, country ways, and Cumberland ale. It was undoubtedly the best September fair ever held.

Life once again settled into the routine of subsistence farming. The nights grew longer and the chill autumn winds whipped through the valley, disturbing all but the sturdiest of man and beast before stilling to allow the onset of the silver fields of frost to proclaim the first of the winter snows. The pace of life slowed, as movement – other than to attend to the immediate needs of shelter and feed for the animals – was tempered by the need of man over that of land. All journeys would now be undertaken by horse alone, the snows being too deep for wheeled transport. Not for the first time, the midst of winter brought on a deep sense of isolation and vulnerability to those in the grip of this freezing confinement.

*

It was early spring before Douglas was eventually to keep his word and call at Freeland. His appearance coincided with our first encounter with an outbreak of cattle plague. It was something that everyone feared, for there was no known cure. Some said it was a curse that had been inflicted upon the valley by disgruntled travellers; others blamed it on contamination of the becks by miners releasing ores and waste material from the works in the mountains; but, whatever its origin, it almost always led to the death of the animal. And so it was that when one of our two cows was found dead, and the second unable to rise from the ground and choking without respite, we and others in the valley lost in a few days what had taken years to acquire. The stench of burning carcasses hung over the land for weeks, a constant reminder of the fragility of our lives. What income we were expecting from the sale of calves was gone; there was nothing to do but wait until summer before replenishing our losses. If we were to continue to provide for ourselves, we would have to go out of the valley and join with the farmer to bring in new stock.

Douglas's arrival in camp, a short distance from Freeland, did not pass without comment. This was not a time to ply his trade or exchange his services for shelter or sustenance. The community had little to offer. For some, his presence just served to reinforce their mistrust of travelling people. For his part, though, Christian fulfilled his promise to show him the mines, and whenever his duties around the farm would allow, the two of them spent time together exploring new ways over the hills into the surrounding valleys.

The disused mines proved to be a valuable source of scrap iron, and with the aid of Christian and the horses, Douglas brought the more serviceable pieces back to his camp. Whenever he could, Christian would watch as Douglas, with his trademark vigour, set about firing and hammering the tangle of metal into tools for the farm, kitchen, and hearth. The apparent ease with which encrusted metal could be shaped into a rough, but serviceable, collection of fire tools, meat hooks, axe heads, and blades or scythes, was fascinating to see. A short while after this, Douglas left to sell what he could outside of the valley; but before he went he shod our horses and presented me with a griddle for the fire. It was a simple gesture, but one which set a bond between us.

Whilst Douglas was away, the farmer with seven other men from the valley, including my husband and Christian, travelled over to Lorton Hall to bring in replacement stock for the cattle lost to the plague. The arrangement had been made for fifty head in all, of which no fewer than twenty were to be heifer calves. On arrival, the condition of the cattle offered was not at all as expected, being as unconscionably poor as the prices were unreasonably high. The ill-tempered bartering went on for days. On more than one occasion the party had withdrawn to return home, only to be persuaded to wait until more cattle had been rounded up for their inspection. In the end, a compromise was reached for forty head at one hundred and seventeen guineas in total. Father settled for a single Longhorn cow with her year-old heifer, which had been less than he had set out to buy, but in the circumstances of a heated and passionate affair, it was, he said, the best available course to take. In truth, the whole party was keen to leave the area and return to Newlands as quickly as possible. Each having made their mark on their chosen animals, they readily set out along the side of Crummock Water, before striking up and across the fells back to what, they all agreed, was a far more welcoming place. As Farmer Bowes had said, it was a sorry day for neighbours when the ills of one were to be taken advantage of by the other. The ways of the past, he lamented, were changing; it was as if custom had fallen prey to commerce in a shameful indictment of neighbourly spirit.

The dearth of cattle grazing the valley's pastures in those few months was not to be wished for; however, it did at least mean that the store of winter feed was high, and work such as the ploughing, draining, and enclosing of new fell pasture had progressed well enough to provide sufficient good quality grazing for the new stock to fatten their bellies. Our sheep had grazed on the higher fells during the summer months, and despite having to sell more than we would have liked, we still had enough remaining ewes to hope for an increased flock come the following spring.

It was to this more hopeful, if not better, place that Douglas returned in the autumn. He came with news that he had entered into an agreement to provide his services as a smith to the farmer, including all those engaged upon the farmer's business, in return for which he was to occupy and equip a disused barn further down the valley. The farmer had agreed to buy what scrap iron could be salvaged from the mine owners until supplies from Maryport in the industrial west of the county could be secured. There was more, too. The farmer had agreed that Christian should be paid sixpence per horse, for each load carried, to transport the iron from the mines to the smithy. All this, Douglas explained, had come about from a chance meeting with the farmer when a cart driven by one of his sons had broken a wheel, leaving him and his passenger stranded not far from the farmer's house in Braithwaite. Douglas had made a temporary binding to the wheel and followed them back home, where, after making good his work, he had been asked if his skills extended to repairing farm equipment, such as a plough. He had said yes, but that he had seen ploughs used elsewhere made with iron, which was more robust and could be sharpened to break up stiffer soils more easily. Given the right working facilities, Douglas had said that he thought this to be the future. The farmer had said nothing at the time but had bought some of his wares before asking him to come back on his return to the valley. This Douglas had done about a month later to be told that all such as was necessary would be made available without charge if he would agree to provide specified repair and replacement services, on the same basis, to the farmer and those in his employment. He would be free to make and sell other wares when not engaged in the farmer's work, and he would be paid for agreed additional new work which brought improvement either to property or farming equipment. All things considered, Douglas explained, he had thought the arrangement a good one, and after agreeing on the carriage terms on behalf of Christian, he had signed a letter of agreement there and then.

The news was indeed welcomed, certainly by ourselves, and as it spread throughout the valley, by most of the local community, too. It was seen as some small recompense for the loss of customary grazing rights brought about by the increasing enclosure of the most fertile common land. If the farmer kept his word and provided us all with tools as well as bearing the cost of repairs, or better still, replacing worn-out equipment, then perhaps our lot would improve. There were those, on the other hand, who saw no good coming from anything to do with the growing intrusion of iron into the rural heritage. What right had a rover, they asked, to favours from the farmer? Hope was therefore mixed with suspicion; either way, it seemed Douglas would be watched as closely as ever.

*

If the first five years were spent in industrious and willing labour for an unspoken notion of greater good, then the next three saw the reality of hardship settle again on our household. Misfortune had shattered our equilibrium once, now it was about to test us to the limit.

A succession of unseasonal storms in August 1795 damaged crops and property alike, with the result that although market prices were high, the amount of grain fit for sale was low; worse still, the amount available for the needs of our family was beyond our means. We then lost one of our cows after she fell into a swollen beck and couldn't be rescued; despite our efforts, which lasted well into the night, she died where she lay. Our milk yields fell, as did our income from the sale of dairy produce. We were not alone in hardship, but that was poor comfort.

The fifty or so sheep and three cows we had left were well below the number required to sustain a living. The fell pastures, although still granted as a right of common land, were being encroached upon more and more by the farmer seeking replacement pasture for managed grazing as he turned the lower, more fertile, fields over into the more profitable arable economy.

The fells could not sustain grazing before late May at the earliest, and the dependence upon storing enough hay and straw for winter feed and bedding was crucial to our changing way of life. It was a precarious existence, one that threatened all who ceased from hard work, fell ill, or became injured in the course of their labour. There was little respite from adversity amidst the almost continual entreaties and demands from the farmer to return more from the land. This left little option but to clear and plough even more land from the lower fells. This was slow, hard work as it meant the removal of much stone; the resulting rough pasture was often small in area and poor in quality, fit only for grazing or shallow root crops.

The farmer kept to his word, though, and soon Christian was driving a modified plough behind his two horses; the use of an iron blade instead of a wooden board to break the soil meant that heavier ground could now be tilled. More and more land was being put to arable to meet what the farmer said was a national shortage of grain. There was talk of the continuing war with France, fighting in the Channel, and even an invasion of England. Everybody was to play their part, and if that meant the loss of common grazing rights for the national cause, then that was the price to be paid.

The valley's appearance was changing, too. Oak trees were being felled in large numbers as timber was requisitioned to build ships on the coast. Enclosures were starting to have an effect, with the larger fields now being bounded by banks or hedging. Sheep and cattle were being grazed on higher, less fertile pastures, and the number of families making a tolerable living off the land was diminishing; some had even had to leave to seek work in the collieries on the west coast. The number of dwellings lying empty was greater than many could remember in a long time.

We were not born to this life, but we learnt to adapt and

on occasion we also played our part in resisting injustice or the intrusion of unwarranted authority. I remember one such instance concerning an allegation of poaching against the Jameson boys. The Jamesons were close neighbours and when it was known that a constable from Keswick was coming to investigate the charge, my husband and others went, on the widowed mother's behalf, to attest to the good character of her sons. The number of men and the vigour of their representation was enough to persuade the constable that the diminishing number of pheasants on the lord's table was in proportion to the dwindling woodland cover and not the culinary taste of working folk. It was just as well, my husband said later, that the constable did not insist on a search of neighbouring parlours. But if it wasn't for the occasional hare or stray pheasant, the plate of the working man would indeed reflect a hungry countenance more often than the actuality of a wholesome meal.

The Consequence

S o, IT CAME TO pass on the nineteenth day of December
in the year 1798, that the forces around Freeland first
started to amass in a way that would begin to loosen our
grip on this worldly home.

There is no need to reveal the detail of these events, but
by way of explanation it is necessary to show that although
the outcome was by no means certain, it was inevitable
that something would change that day to alter the lives of
all those unfortunate enough to be involved. Timing is not
important except insofar as it paints a picture of events. What
happened could happen at any time that is not occupied by
another energy. Equally, time unfilled is not always a danger,
but in a sense, it is a door left ajar that can, with a will that is
strong enough, be opened to another world that will disrupt
a lifetime in this one. In that context, time as a marker of
events is important; but, time as a measure of continuity
between one event and another, and more significantly, as a
barrier between one place and another, is without purpose
or justification. What was to take place could happen with
or without the accompaniment of time.

I first noticed something amiss when my husband came home early. Even at this time of the year, he and Christian would have been out on the land or around the animal shelters until early evening. In fact, both had been repairing a field boundary when he quietly announced his intention to return back down with the dogs, the same dogs who, for no apparent reason, had been fretting all afternoon.

The decision to go home was instinctive. A spirit under threat will seek shelter from lines of strength or familiar places. Freeland provided both and for a while served to delay the inevitable. The tide was stemmed, but the outcome was unfolding slowly to its inescapable conclusion. The forces that surrounded my husband that evening were immense, but the inherent energy within Freeland rendered them devoid of malice, thus securing a peaceful conclusion. By returning to a natural line of strength in his life, he had cushioned what otherwise might have been more traumatic. He died at around seven in the evening, just as Christian walked into the yard.

*

The death of his father once more ripped our family apart and exposed the fragile mask of security for the second time in Christian's life. His heart became harder and colder than the granite that bore witness to our life in this bleak terrain. I mourned the loss of a husband and father as only one who realises the burden of such a sudden death can. My grief was all the more intense for the concern I felt for my son; the pain I carried was for us both. There had been no warning. Instead, there were now two where there had been three.

The sequence of events that led to our family settling in Freeland was not part of some greater plan and bore no connection to what might be called just reward for endeavour and fortitude. However, neither was it fate. Fate is no more than an expression for allaying the fear of the unknown, for denying a part played, a course taken, or for escaping reality and not seeking an explanation of how events conspire to the conclusion they do. Fate is a convenience for those unwilling to know their part in life.

Had earlier events been different or had priorities been other than they were, so that my husband had not been where he was, the conclusion would also have been different. It may have been the same in outcome but postponed in time, or it may have been completely averted had some earlier fateful course not have been chosen. The possible permutations as to what could have taken place that day are infinite, and as with all events, there are innumerable possible outcomes. For example, the one in which the reader is now reading my story is different from that in which the same person is not; of the two given courses only one is possible, and it will be as the result of choice – allowing for the fact that the series of events and elections leading up to such a moment were as they were required to be to place each party in relation to the other.

It is not just that the reader has made a choice to read or not read this tale, it is simply one of many outcomes that are possible given that two things exist and are placed close to each other. Where one of the two has a will, then a choice is inevitable, and one of the possible outcomes will become a present reality and thereafter an indelible record of choice: an imprint and a stepping stone for the future of both. It is this selection, this wilful intervention, that creates a moment in time from what otherwise would have remained undisturbed, a condition of harmony between the two. It is this harmony, this equilibrium, that is so important in knowing the fullness and reason for what occurs in life.

For a moment, consider also the scenarios where one or other or both of the aforementioned objects do not exist, and further where each exists but in a different space; in which latter case the assertion would be – given that one has a will – that a choice is not required and neither impacts upon the other nor do they jointly influence the present or future of each other.

Such an argument for choice would be just, were choice dependent upon the deliberations of a conscious mind alone. However, should there be another presence that engages in the relationship, then choice and its consequences would no longer be so straightforward.

It is this relationship between two or more things that may or may not lead to a dependency of one, or each, upon the other. It is the outcome of this dependency that is sometimes assumed to be fate, and it is fate – or luck, that may often pass as reason when in truth the reason for all things lies solely with wilful creatures. This is undeniably so, but again not as may be assumed through the deliberations of the conscious mind alone.

In the fullness of time I would come to understand all these truths, but for the moment such understanding was beyond my thought and comprehension.

*

The months that followed were hard. At first, Christian tried to continue in his father's footsteps. The farmer's cattle were fed and calves were taken to market. However, Christian was not a stockman; gradually the wellbeing of the animals deteriorated to the extent that the farmer discontinued our agreement for care of his stock. The reputation his father had built suffered so that our trade declined and the smallholding went from being the main source of income to a liability.

With the exception of two cows and the horses, our stock had to be sold. The outbuildings once again started to fall into a state of disrepair as the income from labouring and seasonal working of the horses went on feed and upkeep of the animals. There was now no regular income for household or living expenses. I resorted to taking in mending and sewing, and supplemented that small income by spinning, winding yarn, and baking and selling bread, but it was by no means sufficient. It was on one such occasion when selling the last of a batch of loaves that the thought of bread into wine came to me. For years I had mashed barley ale for my husband, and it now seemed natural to do the same for others. To begin with, it was a few occasional gallons, but soon neighbours were placing orders until eventually I was persuaded to open up one of the outbuildings for the men to use as a drinking room. This, in turn, led to the regular sale of alcohol from the parlour of the house on a Thursday and Friday between seven o'clock and ten o'clock in the evening. It was this compromise between the Devil and the Church that finally won me over. I likened myself to the fowl once again roaming free in the yard. The Free Goose had risen from the ashes.

Evocation

I MUST SAY THAT I have not hesitated to relay my part in this story; my journal has been faithfully recounted and I have relived events from afar with some pleasure and a little pride at overcoming what seemed so troublesome to me at the time.

My journal, though, cannot account for what did not concern me or for what I failed to understand at the time of writing. So, my search still required more from me, it required the fullest disclosure of all events encircling my loss so that I might achieve peace of mind.

How can such hidden confidences be uncovered? It is a question I have asked myself many times, and yet by the gift of grace and the blessing of kindred souls I have come to the understanding I craved.

From here, my story is intertwined with those I hold most dear and with that which guides my hand. I trust in God and believe in His mercy.

*

Sunday morning was star bright and brutally cold; temperatures were well below freezing and there was a stillness that comes with the sort of weather that slows the natural rhythm of life. Extreme heat or cold seems to induce a soporific effect on life to the extent that a spiritual silence bears down upon the unnatural fanfare of the normal day. Christian could hear his father's words when anyone commented on the weather: 'It is a blessing on us all; a gift to life without dues or expectation.' This was said no matter what the day brought. However, this day was a blessing we could all have done without. This was one of those occasions where choice is tightly bound to what has gone before, so that even if he had known what was to come, Christian would have found it extremely difficult to do other than follow his resolve to continue with their quest.

The hour before dawn was not a time either Christian or Douglas were used to. The natural rhythms of the body that come from generations close to the soil were stilled so that neither was fully attuned to the clock that played with the degrees of light between night and day. They failed to appreciate the simple beauty of moments that bridged time between the fading forces of the unseen, more spiritual, world and the emerging energies of the less mystical, physical world. As ever, there was a witness to everything, and those present and competing for the right to take their place in life were there to observe the start of one more day.

The first anticipatory shiver stole a shortened breath from Christian's lungs as the pair moved away from the shelter of the Free Goose. Muffled both to the cold and sounds around them, it was only the eagle high on its ledge and the hare in its winter coat low in the crystallised grasses that detected the gathering horde in their footsteps. The scent of emptiness in both their minds was an enticing lure. In contrast, the instincts of the hare and eagle were sharper at any hour than Douglas's or Christian's, and right now they were screaming danger as the shadows lengthened behind them.

They travelled light, each with a slung bundle of rope plus a single staff – or mountain stick as they first called it – fashioned from ash in the likeness of a shortened shepherd's crook. It was Douglas who had replaced the crook with a forged point and adze, in the style of a till, to gouge out steps and holds in virgin slabs of snow.

Neither spoke. They were not yet inclined to think about the beauty of the morning, the danger of their expedition or their preparedness for the moment. The same reticence that typified their discussions had bled into their character.

Their path from the Free Goose followed the road to Stair for a short way. The stars in the heavens jigged their spangled dance in the ice-mirrors of rutted tracks as their nailed boots scratched and spat their way up the steady incline away from their lives in the valley below.

Still, no words had been exchanged. Each was submissive to the rhythms of time and space around them. Neither recognised the impact they had on events; nor did they notice the presence of the wagon driver and his horses, who had travelled the same road only hours before, and who – equally unwittingly – had left both physical and non-physical traces of their journey.

The physical signs left by the earlier travellers were clear to see, had either Christian or Douglas been inclined to heed the recent past of the road they now trod. The ruts left by the wagon's wheels were deep, more so on the exposed valley-side of the road. In contrast, the horseshoe prints were deeper on the hill-side of the road, indicating their struggle to haul an unevenly loaded wagon. Every so often, the horses would be straightened by the wagonmaster, only to have the wagon slide once more towards the valley. Again, the horses' instinct to correct the imminent danger would lead them to turn towards the opposite side of the road. And thus, it went on; man against beast, toiling in opposition, each countering the other's view.

The intangible trail left by the passing travellers was less clear, but nonetheless informative, if only to the gathering shadows around the pair. The scent – as I have called it – left by the horses and absorbed in turn by the natural elements on and around the road, was predominantly one of fear. Not without cause was this road known as dangerous to those who used it regularly. Tales of injury and mishap were passed from traveller to traveller, and in turn the apprehension of man was converted into the spiritual mark of the place. Cattle, sheep, horses, and dogs, as well as the free-ranging wildlife, would react to the scent left by humans with that of their own so that the cycle was continuously renewed and enforced on every journey and occasion that witnessed occupation of the road.

*

The use of the word 'scent' can only serve as a poor description of reality. The air of attraction I describe is not as an odour on the wind, as in the secretions of animal humours, nor is it the telltale trails left by the fleeting passage of mortal form on physical matter. These outward signals are merely gateways into deeper, darker registers of heartbeats left in the wake of time as a record of events that define us all. This absorption of history deep into the mineral structure of nature has been continuous since the birth of matter itself. The cataclysmic origin of the physical world, so many years ago, should be likened to the creation of the first page of the first chapter in the first-ever Book of Life; a book where pages are elements and ink is time passing, sometimes pausing to rest on the cellular lattice-worked parchment. A book that *can* be read, although with increasing difficulty, as words are confused with loss and destruction of pages, and the fading of the story as time moves on and the ink fades. Each period and event in history has been recorded through the physical and metaphysical impact it has on all life; a legacy footprint on the elements that surrounded it and thereafter remain. As the reader may begin to appreciate, such a book, if indeed it were to take the form of a book, would be unimaginably large, decipherable by few, and mastered by none.

The parallel with a book for recording history is, for the moment, the best I can manage. However, whereas a book can be opened and read at will, the understanding of our past, how it impacts on our present, and the alternatives that are offered for the future, cannot so easily be illustrated with the same analogy. For the moment, though, it is enough to rest on the magnitude of the proposition and dwell on the thought that the physical being also comprises natural elements; it is therefore at one and the same time, a contributor to and – was it of a mind and ability so to become – a student of, such a volume of knowledge. A student, who can only yearn in vain for a guide to free the mind from the dullness of its senses.

As it was, neither Douglas nor Christian was inclined to receive such signals from the road they now trod. Years of evolution had all but erased their affinity with the natural forces around them. Certainly, they felt pain and physical discomfort as easily as the next man; they also recognised danger as something unusual or exceptional to that which they were used to. But, in all these instances, the range of their perception was less than it had been for their ancestors and less than it could have been for them had they wished to travel with Nature rather than walk through it. The dark and cold compounded their lack of sensitivity. Naivety is a fickle companion when set against danger.

*

They successfully topped the rise away from the last of the sleepy outlines of occupation. They left the road and headed onto the pearl-white fells. For the first time, they stopped to acknowledge the beauty around them.

'Fair ol' morning.'

The words hung between them waiting for a companionable response.

'Could be,' was just enough to satisfy pleasantries as well as to acknowledge the likely probability of the abbreviated weather forecast and, less mechanically, to express the apprehension they both now harboured. It was very cold.

The first phosphorescent threads of silver were just offering the faintest of silhouettes across the valley's mists to the distant snowy peaks. This pageantry, played so delicately to seasonal variations, was not to be so lightly dismissed by mere time-travellers.

'Remarkable,' said Christian, stumbling to express the fleeting intensity of feeling that poured into his soul.

Douglas refrained from mocking his friend's growing eulogy; his respectful silence and almost imperceptible upward motion of his head to Christian's enquiring gaze conceded the point.

'Best be off then.'

Half-turning in readiness to move, Christian felt an eternal chill rip through his veins. It was as if some glacial dagger had pierced his lungs and plunged deep into his soul. His pulse and all about him slowed: frozen in body and paralysed of thought, in the slow motion of a nightmare he witnessed the fearsome spectre of his father turning back down the hill away from his work. Again and again the silent image presented itself as some portent of horror to arrest his progress and divert his course. A strangled gasp of disbelief escaped from within to check the assault. He turned away, and in doing so lost that which he had fleetingly known. He had chosen to doubt and would not be shown again.

*

This brief encounter with the power of the unending self was disturbing; he had chosen not to acknowledge its presence or the effect it had upon him. Denying that something exists does not disprove its existence.

*

The screams of his father's tortured spirit waned pitifully on the silence of his denial. Douglas was already well into his stride. It was easier to follow than question, and so Christian fell into line and sustained the pattern of despair on the path they now trod.

The dry cold of the higher valley closed in on him. The lightness of foot he regularly felt in these places was now replaced by leaden soles so heavy that he felt as if with every step he was being drawn into the depths of an underworld mire. It was getting darker – despite the onset of dawn.

Their path drew them further away from the expanse and fullness of air in the open valley floor below. They were now moving into the confines and strictures of the cloistered high-mountain terrain. The choice of route was no longer theirs alone. They were guided by Nature's whims: the playfulness and foregoing of order, the disdain of design and the abandonment of array as the arm of Creation wrestled with the scouring forces of age. Douglas intuitively assessed the lie of the incline before them: granite projections, protruding mounds of snow, troughs and scurries that might indicate easier going, but which could easily hide dangerous pits for careless travellers. Some long-forgotten ancestral legacy led him effortlessly over the contours, seemingly without a clear point of arrival in mind; as ever with those gifted with co-ordination between mind and physical adeptness, his progress was swift. Christian opted to follow rather than to pioneer his own course; he had long since learnt not to deviate from his friend's footprints. The contrast between their progress was noticeable but didn't impede their journey. Douglas's step was lighter, his pace more regular, and his mind more focused on the seemingly simple objective of moving across the land without deviating from his goal or risk to himself. Christian, in contrast, laboured to follow his companion; his movements were heavy and his mind divided. He occasionally turned to convince himself he had imagined that which in his heart he knew he had not.

The option to turn around and emerge unscathed from their course was always there, but neither of them would do so voluntarily. The idea of abandoning the trip due to sensitivity – or worse, fear – was without precedent and faintly amusing, Christian thought. It would certainly shatter the adventuresome image he had of himself and he could not begin to picture the ridicule of others. He needed this sense of achievement, this sense of knowing what was possible, to be able to live with himself. There was no choice in the matter.

His movements became more wearisome. He tried to focus on Douglas's footprints to recover some sort of rhythm to his step. He saw the perfect outline of a boot where it had briefly settled into starched ground. He noted the hallucinatory disappearance and reappearance of stud marks left in the base of the mould as his own boot hung and then fell into each new cast, only for another impression to reappear in an enticingly easy trail of homage and imitation. Minutes passed as he drifted in a haze of attentive inattention. Momentarily, he was free from the higher distractions of emotion and reason, and perilously unaware of the value of both. Slowly, his gait became more metronomic. He started to regain his balance. He began to link sight to sound. Then, on the cusp of recovery, came the inglorious fall from the semblance of sound mind and reasonable behaviour. The full shame of it – the inexplicable, unexpected disturbance to direction and attitude was instant, final and unforgiving.

*

It was in that instant of reconnection between body and mind that Christian witnessed that first fleeting, vaporous sense of having travelled without knowledge of the journey. There was a detachment, a loneliness in the absence of feeling from a silent mind. It was, however, no more and no less than time lost, moments that evade consciousness to remain forever private. It was a rare glimpse of life within life, one that is normally so repressed as to remain invisible to the physical mind. It is the moment of reawakening that evokes the sense of sleepwalking or passing through time without memory.

*

Christian knew exactly what had happened. It seemed as clear as if he had been watching the whole event from two paces behind. He also had a pretty good idea as to what was going to happen next. That bothered him a lot more.

'What the bloody 'eck's up?'

It was too late. He relaxed his efforts to resume an upright position.

'Ice.' He lied.

Douglas turned and set off once more.

'Daft bugger.' He muttered.

A teasing wisp of wind flicked snow against his face as he raised his crumpled form to follow his accuser's footprints. This was now a path that the two of them no longer trod alone, with tracks in which no human foot rested free of unseen sanction. For now, he was safe. The first attempt, if that was what it was, had failed, and the malevolent coalition would take time to reassemble its forces into another fore-chosen place.

The Gully

T HE WAY NOW BECAME steeper as the dark outcrops
morphed into the black buttresses and columns that
fronted the domed outline of Dale Head. The snow-filled
gullies beckoned seductively as corridors of escape between
the harsh lines of granite peaks. It was terrifying and
breath-taking: the eye-catching scenery and the growing
isolation of higher altitude were at once a distraction and a
relief from the fractured events of the morning so far. The
black-and-white imagery sharpened the gradation of fell
to mountain and hid the pastel palette of highland colour
from the traveller's eye. The whole effect was disorientating
and contributed to the slow mummification of the senses,
shamed as they were by this greater presence.

Christian bathed in radiated glory. If there was any
more impressive sight or pleasing place of wonder, he
thought, he had yet to behold it. All other vales and heights
were by way of a gateway to this crowning throne of beauty.
It had always been so, ever since his early wanderings had
first led him to stumble across this scene, and like a true
friend it would always be there when needed.

*

This sensory journey, blessed as it appeared to be, was always going to be broken – an exceptional moment in what was to become the bleakest hour of life. A respite that summons affinity with some unheralded calling may be described as a window in time that reconnects the eternal being to his ancestors: to a past life lived within a spiritual lattice that served to nurture the human form from unnatural intrusions. Such encounters were then acknowledged and attended as unfathomable truths: codes that served to temper the gulf between unseen forces and the naked susceptibility of man to the allurement of temporal distractions.

A wind that teases and molests in an attempt to check the traveller's progress is in itself not a force to fear. But to disregard the message conveyed is another matter. The same gossamer that delivers a flickering alarm can, if dismissed out-of-hand, vengefully cast the final telling surge that loosens the wayfarer's step from his path.

Christian had been told and unwittingly had heard. But he was not of a time that readily acknowledged the wisdom of caution. Nor was he able or prepared to voice his inner feelings of doubt. Once again, his independence and trust in knowing only what he could see was overriding his inner voice.

*

He set off to follow the diminishing figure of Douglas. The silhouetted manikin was now gaining height across the snowfield that led to the start of their climb. He told himself the change to the firmer snow on the higher slope would be a welcome relief to the plunging softness he was finding so difficult to master. Slowly, he gained the ground he sought and felt the hardening snow lighten his pace. He straightened his back, allowing his breath to come more easily. As he lifted his head to check his progress, his senses rose from the study of his own turmoil to focus on the day's objective.

The half-light of the distant dawn was now reflected in the sky above him. It was enough to sharpen the towering, corniced ridge against the misty morning. The snow beneath his feet reflected the new day's shafts of light; he felt emboldened by his returning powers of observation and the opening of the way before him.

With his staff now planted on the upward slope he again began to trace the steps of his friend. This was the reason he climbed; this was why he lived, and this was where he found peace. Like others, he laboured and fought to live in this wild country, but it could also nurture a tortured body to provide a canvas for the spirit to rise from within and herald nature's beauty. He had heard of artists who would travel to these hills to capture the scenery in paint and crayon to project a likeness for others to marvel at; but surely no man-made image, however bold or grand, could compete with nature's moods – in tempest or tranquillity – to create a sense of humility and wonder in those seeking comfort in these high reflections.

He drove forward, rejoicing in the sound of crisp snow settling beneath his boots. At last, a rhythm to his step. The warmth was returning to his bare hands, warding off the chill grip of the dry air. The release from the confines below had freed him from his crazed shackles; he was definitely more suited to the open spaces before him.

His progress was steady and the effort required well within his capabilities. He soon drew close to where Douglas was standing on the margin of the jagged buttress they needed to traverse to reach their destination. A firm clasp of the hand hauled him onto a low ledge. Douglas had already uncoiled their rope.

'Best we join up from here. There's more ice than last time.'

Christian nodded, and noted Douglas had already bound his hands with sacking. He followed his friend's example before removing his own shorter coils of rope from over his shoulder. He passed one to Douglas to tie around his waist and did the same for himself with the other. The twelve foot of woven hemp would pass around his waist to give three good bands, which when tied would leave a looped end on which to attach the climbing rope. The use of rope in this manner was a technique they had come to by way of trial and error. When they had first started climbing, Douglas carried a rope to haul Christian up the more difficult stretches, but then they would find they had gone different ways and when he lowered the rope it would pull Christian off – or worse, wouldn't reach him at all and leave him back-tracking like some 'orphaned wretch on a dung heap'. They had then resorted to tying up before climbing so that they would both go the same way, but that invariably meant that one would threaten the other by moving 'too quickly' or 'too slowly'. In the end, they had agreed that the current arrangement was best whereby Douglas led before calling Christian to follow. By chance, this had also provided a degree of safety, when, on one occasion, the trailing rope had caught in a rock fissure and alerted them to the possibility of using such an anchor to protect them both in the event of one or the other slipping.

'I've cleared somewhere for you to stand – just round the corner,' said Douglas. 'Ready?'

Christian nodded and ran the rope through his hands until only a few feet remained between them.

Douglas moved off, kicking away ice and snow for foot purchase and occasionally scraping handholds with his staff. He soon moved out of sight and began working his way up and around the craggy promontory. This was the third time he had led this stretch, and whilst he wasn't sure he was following either one of the previous routes, he began to recognise the snow-filled nooks and remember the exposed corners of rock. His hands drifted back and forth across the rough canvas as he instinctively probed for holds.

His progress was steady, gaining height easily on rock that seemed to him to have a profusion of strong holds and comforting gaps in which to wedge feet and hands. He paused to clear snow from a cleft behind a jagged piece of rock that would serve well as the first anchor. He looped a coil over the top and spoke as though Christian were standing next to him.

'I'm pulling in loose rope … I've found an anchor.'

Christian knew the routine. He allowed all the rope, bar two or three feet, to be hauled up before responding.

'That's it! No more.'

'Right.'

Douglas acknowledged the tension on the rope. He removed the loop from behind the rock and replaced it with the taut line in his hand. If needs must, he thought, Christian could now pull himself up. As he loosely wound the coiled rope, now hanging below him, over his shoulders, he guessed the remaining length.

'Twenty feet left. Stay where you are. I'm moving off.'

Without waiting for a reply, he turned to continue his upward progress. He had already formulated a plan. Despite his euphoria as he climbed, he was aware that Christian would be getting cold; from his experience of his friend's way of thinking, he knew he would be anxious to be getting on with the job.

They didn't have enough rope to go straight through to the foot of the gully, but he wanted to make sure they didn't stop too often. He'd be as direct as he could with his line of approach. As he climbed he would slip a coil from his shoulders to trail behind him like an umbilical cord to nowhere. As the weight from his back transferred to the arc below, he knew he would soon have to find a suitable place from which to bring Christian up. He was also aware that the rope was catching a lot of snow and was becoming heavy and stiff with ice. He paused again, trying to spot a clear change in angle in the profile of snow and rock against the white backdrop of the mountain top. There was nothing obvious. Reluctant to deviate significantly up or down for no good reason, he chose to maintain his current angle of ascent; if necessary, he would contrive a platform out of the snow with his staff. He focused on the simple, short movements required to move around the buttress: probing, kicking, and shifting his balance from one foot to the other, his arms comfortably extended, his hands not unnecessarily high above his eye line. He eased his way upward, seeking freedom from gravity.

This was the way he and Christian had first learnt to crawl their way over the small rocky outcrops in the valley below. Those early days, as he recalled, were warm in weather as well as in companionship. By introducing him to the miners and the ready availability of scrap iron, Christian had been instrumental in persuading him to give up his wanderings and settle to his passion for forging new tools. As their confidence had grown, they had progressed to scrambling and then to more serious encounters with steeper rock faces, until they had progressed from an awkward attachment to the hills to an easier, elegant empathy with them, as they moved across their contours.

'How's it going?'

The shout from below conveyed more than a general enquiry as to progress. He sensed the impatience of Christian who by now would be stiffening with cold and inaction. The frustration carried on the words made him hasten to secure a resting place.

'A few more feet!' he responded, more in hope and good intention than truth – one foothold was as good as another at the moment. He started to clear a step on a mound of snow he hoped would have a foundation of rock beneath. It allowed him to lean out to scrape away at the face – there were good holds but nothing that would take a rope. He probed lower, the point of his staff seeking the weakness he needed. At last, a suggestion of space between the layers of rock that he could clear and force the shaft a few inches into the recess to give that precious anchor. It would have to do. Half-crouching, he looped the last length of rope over the end of the staff, eased it down the shaft and pulled; he convinced himself it would hold. There was nothing more he could do until Christian had freed more rope by releasing the anchor below. It was now his turn to wait. He turned and with his back now braced against the rock allowed himself a self-congratulatory smile of victory before passing on the news.

'I'm settled. Come on up, let me know when you reach the anchor.'

The response was immediate.

'I'm moving!'

For Douglas, the adventure began when the climbing started. That was where lay the challenge to his strength and his resolve to find a way past seemingly insurmountable obstacles. The physical test was what drew him to the hills. It was an effrontery to his manhood to be surrounded by such giants and not to accept the daily invitation to duel. He knew Christian's view was different. It was more respectful, more reverential – seeing beauty and majesty where he saw brutality and menace. The two viewpoints were contradictory; that was of no concern, it would not be the last occasion. However, he also recognised that between them they held a more complete picture, sharing two halves of the whole story, of which neither had sole rights to the truth.

He could hear Christian below, battering the rock into submission, as if he were trying to bury himself in its sanctuary. Was he the only one who noticed the anger, he wondered. The forcefulness of his friend's determination to cling to this pedestal was uncharacteristic of his gentler nature. Unlike his own lighter, easier approach, Christian's frantic chiselling was like someone trying to break down the gates of Hades.

'You'll waken it up, my friend,' he whispered; then louder, more helpfully, 'Nice work. Nearly there!'

He glanced to his right and began to picture his next line of attack, picking out a break in the profile which angled away to what might be a decent ledge. How had he not noticed it earlier? Probably something to do with the light and the need to get that sheep-man below up and moving.

'Pull in!' Christian's shout brought him back to the moment.

He hauled until he felt resistance. He would now maintain the tension on the rope to keep it out of the way of Christian's flailing staff. The battering started again. He could see the shower of ice and snow being expelled from below. It was the same in summer, only then it was stone and vegetation that was excavated. That was one of the reasons he preferred to lead. Snowballs were one thing, but rock falling on him was another matter altogether. Besides, he wasn't good at following.

'Ah, it was you making that clatter. I wondered who it could be!'

A few feet more and Christian was as close as he could get.

'Not much I know, but look at the view,' he offered. He failed to notice his friend's inquisitive look.

Douglas shuffled out of his refuge, willing his blood to start circulating again.

'I'll take your staff, it might be better up there,' he gestured. 'I'll bring you up if it is!'

When Christian was settled Douglas moved off once more. Dawn was fully up, the light of a new day detailing fresh weaknesses in the mountain's armoury. His movements were assured and, as he intended, an education to Christian below. There was competition between them, and for Douglas such opportunities were there to parade their differences. He reached a narrow ledge. It was indeed a better position than the one he had just had to accept, but he could see the base of their final objective and was reluctant to linger.

'It's alright, but we're nearly there,' he volunteered, 'what do you think?'

'Keep going. I'm fine.'

It was the response he wanted.

'Shan't be long then; we're more than halfway.'

It looked straightforward: a short horizontal traverse around the side of the buttress, followed by a sharply inclined dog-leg up to the entrance of the gully. Giving himself some slack and with a nod to Christian, he eased himself away from the comfort of the ledge. He felt a pang of guilt for his own earlier shortcoming in not securing a better refuge for his friend. Next time he would be stronger; he wouldn't accept second best from the mountain.

Douglas continued tracing what natural contours of the rock he could see, stepping from one line to the next only where he thought an opportunity presented itself. It was a style he was comfortable with; even under slabs of snow and ice he could discern the shape of folds in the rock. He had long since persuaded himself that snow would only rest in a place where there was purchase and he was now testing that belief to the limit. Ice, though, was another matter. He was relying heavily on his boots to shatter the frozen shield that guarded his chosen course. He wedged the rope behind a small lump of rock. This was no anchor, but it might take some weight off the rope, he thought, as he pulled what he could of the trailing rope out and over the partially cleared chase.

The climbing rope would chafe, but that would at least free some of the ice that was now forcing him to haul slack every few yards to overcome the added weight. He judged that the next dozen or so moves would see him at the base of the dog-leg, the final challenge before entering the gully itself. If anything, the ice was thicker on this face; he focused on deepening the handholds where he couldn't break through to the rock below. The ribbed pattern of iced fangs, hanging in time like some huge old man's encrusted beard, had transformed the face of saturated rock they had so reluctantly turned away from on their last attempt. It was an altogether wilder and more fitting mask for a craggy old mountain. He knocked away more rivulets of ice, hearing the daggers ricocheting to oblivion on the gargoyled crags below. His outstretched arm sought a momentary purchase, enough to claw him up and across the worst of the petrified flow. His feet briefly shared the same space, before, with two sure low arcs of his staff, he cut away enough of a toe-hold to step back onto the ice fall to secure a more balanced position. He knew Christian would add to his chiselling in his own way later, so he shifted his balance again and edged away from the worst of the armoured screen.

After some extensive clearing, the ledge he had been targeting at the foot of the dog-leg was wider than he imagined. Given his earlier experience, he concluded it would provide a timely physical and mental respite before tackling the gully itself. He also recalled his numbness at not being able to move at the first stop; by now Christian would be frozen. He swiftly secured his position and relayed the news to his friend. He could detect the relief in the response – a mixture of awakening from the imaginings of a stranded castaway and the anticipation of a child who had been promised a day at the fair – if he was good. In practice, though, expectation had long since been neutralised by the cold.

The hesitant, quiet, 'Take up slack,' was no more than perfunctory.

Christian's words were as far from an expression of relief as were his frozen limbs from moving from his enforced imprisonment. His mind was ready but his arms and legs were not. They had been bound to the mountain by unseen shackles and he fleetingly believed his fate was to stay forever in the clutches of unknown forces from the depths of a bitter mountain. A jolt at his waist freed his mind and tongue.

'Wait!' he half-screamed, half-howled, 'WAIT!'

Startled by his involuntary cry, Christian looked about for the source of the anguish. In so doing he only just managed to grasp hold of the taut rope to follow the lifeline up and away from his frozen tomb. He had been petrified to the spot. Had he observed the place to which he had been bound, he would have noticed the outline of his form etched in its crystallised casket.

Douglas had heard the wail well up from below and had not related the source to his friend. The sharp tug on the rope that followed, though, most definitely was. He braced himself for the full weight of a man, but mercifully was not called to test his or the rope's strength.

'Are you alright?' he shouted.

'Fine. I'm coming up.'

Douglas had never followed Christian on a difficult climb. He reflected on the apparent inequalities in the two roles; not for the first time, he questioned the reluctance of Christian to lead. Had he been too brutal in his mocking of his friend's awkward style? It was odd that one so sensitive should be so bullish when it came to the physical side of things. He was in awe of Christian's learning and understanding of nature, but at a loss to explain why he couldn't pick the obvious routes across a fell or up a crag. After all, he was supposed to earn his living from the land. He glanced up at the route ahead. He would suggest that Christian be the first to the gully entrance. It was short, not too difficult, and he would be in sight all the way up.

He heard the crack of forged metal on the millennia of creation. He marvelled at the ferocity of his friend's determination to cling to the most inaccessible of terrain in pursuit of his pleasure. What joy it was to witness from his godlike pulpit another's endeavour to survive.

'Thou'st best leave some for miners to come back to,' he laughed.

Christian had heard it all before, but was pleased with the good humour.

'If thee'd done thy job right in first place, I wouldna hav' to be doin' all this work,' he retaliated.

Douglas smiled – after all, he thought, that last stretch had been mildly interesting.

He seized the moment as Christian hauled himself onto the ledge.

'Thou'st done well. Carry on through?' He pointed out the route with a sweep of his hand. 'I'll take run up gully.'

Christian nodded. He could see the route clearly – it would save both time and effort in changing over. He kicked the ice from his boots and adjusted his waistband.

'I'm climbing.'

He reached for the first exposed angle of rock and placed the sole of his boot against a protruding slab; leaning back he eased up until he was able to hook the end of his staff into the near vertical fissure that defined the natural progression upwards. His left hand sought the same crack, allowing him to shoulder his staff and rely solely on touch to feel the textures and forms above.

Slowly, he started to find a rhythm; hesitant, cautious, but sure. He had already picked out a likely looking place for the first anchor from below. He wedged himself alongside a jagged spur of rock and felt the most simple, pleasurable sense of achievement he had experienced yet that day. He had forgotten the horrors of earlier: the vexing images of his father, the self-doubt, and the appalling struggle with the recurring portents of tragedy. This was what he was seeking from these excursions to the wilderness. If he were asked why he should want to expose himself to the isolation and dangers of the fells, he would have an answer in today's tale of conquest: it was the joy of achievement coupled with friendship.

The final leg to the gully was no more difficult than walking across the yard at home, or that was how it felt to Christian. However, the step into the mouth was more awkward, requiring a scramble on all fours over displaced rocks and small boulders that had been brought to a standstill by the pinched opening. Those pursed lips were now cast with a mantle of serrated snow talons. They spat shards of steely defiance as he cleaved out their final refuge.

Douglas had been silently admiring the commanding ease of Christian's ascent, right up to the point of return to the more familiar battering: the shower of feathered fangs bouncing off the rocks around him.

'Hold hard. Enough! I have no shield broad enough to defend myself,' he cursed. 'Raise me up!'

*

The two stood side by side. For the first time, they surveyed the gully above them. Christian held his breath. A silence such as hitherto known only to cloistered monks dared him to move. An air of monastic denial froze his mind. It was the peace of eternal suspension, the most wondrous of all beauties, and they were to be the first to defile it. Neither of them had the breath or the words to describe the majesty and power of the glacial stillness they had stumbled upon. What would normally be a dark, craggy, rock-littered gully had been transformed by spiralling winter winds into a barrel-smooth passage of iridescent ice. The near luminous greens and blues before them faded away as their gaze lifted to the colourless, steely grey silvers of the entombed granite above, before, higher still, cooling to a white-necked ruff with inset golden jewels, glistening as the rays of morning sunlight streamed into the gully at its head. They were truly in the presence of the mountain gods; they had been granted sole rights to a display of the glory of primeval creation. This was no place for mortals.

'We're done for,' whispered Christian. 'We have to turn back.'

Silence stood close by, denying his words, freezing the need to think. It was the most precious stillness, devoid of all intrusions and distractions. No eye could hope to see its end, no ear could reach its furthest part; all was as a white light streaming into their souls.

Sacrilege.

'Douglas?'

'It's all right. There is a way – we're not going back.'

Douglas turned. Christian saw the blanched look of

someone whose world had been shattered, but who would not, or could not, accept it.

'I'll cut steps. I'll use both staves, cut steps, and when I reach the top you'll untie and I'll lower the staves back down to you. It's the only way.'

A confusion of sense and insanity swirled inside Christian's head, jumbling Douglas's words in a delirium of sights and sounds. This is madness, he thought. No one has ever seen such a miraculous sight and now he proposes to destroy it?

'We can't – '

Douglas didn't let him finish: 'Don't worry. It'll be alright.'

'It's not the …' Christian hesitated. He wanted to say that climbing had nothing to do with it, that the real point here was respect, humility, recognition, an understanding that they were in the presence of a power greater than themselves. This was no ordinary landscape. Even if they climbed it, their success would be hollow. Such achievements were not theirs to tell, or boast about, or even remember as a victory over a worthy foe. This would be blasphemy; it would weigh on them forever.

He tried again.

'Please, Douglas. If you value my friendship, don't do this.'

Douglas straightened. Just for a moment, he hesitated.

'Christian. It will be alright. You know I value your friendship more than anything. We can do this. We will both be stronger when this is done. You'll see.'

He placed his hand on Christian's shoulder and turned

away. In doing so he failed to notice the blood drain from his friend's face and the telltale look of despair in his eyes.

Christian couldn't watch as the first crack of metal on ice echoed around him. Each subsequent incursion, now fused with the crunch of nailed boot plunging into shallow wounds to create wedge-shaped toeholds, left its indelible print on his mind. Mechanically, he began to let out the rope leading to his friend. He knew there would be no protection left in the gully. This was it. There was no turning back.

Something had been lost from the day; something taken from him. The disagreement with Douglas was one thing, there was always rivalry between them and often conflict; invariably he gave way, suppressing his own will for – as he thought – the benefit of them both. But today was different. On the one hand, he had just taken the lead to get to their goal, an accomplishment that had boosted his confidence, but he had failed to dissuade Douglas from continuing. He wasn't ambivalent about it. It wasn't the difficulty that concerned him, it was purely the grace and good sense of submission to a higher calling – something he had so often done before for the two of them. But, now, when it really mattered, he had failed to articulate that this time it was not about them. This time, he knew they were in the presence of something far greater than their own wilful exuberance; this time, they had been led to the limit of life's decree. They had been found wanting.

*

What my son had lost, I believe, was the belief in his generous absoluteness; that moment when the body prevails over the spirit to declare a new order. He had lost touch with his inner presence: the code that binds our conscience and sets our character had been broken. The disconnection between his beliefs and actions stretched his capacity to act with any sort of credible account, to the extent that his demeanour had become one of despair at his own shortcomings.

In time, these anxieties would have passed. His spirit would have recovered. However, one thing Christian did not have was time. Not only was he now mindfully ill-prepared for what lay ahead, but he was also unwittingly unleashing the power that had been plaguing his mind all morning. Such forces of darkness are powerless without a cause to give rise to their venom. What had begun as mischief was to become an occasion of opportunistic fury. Douglas's strength of character and Christian's disaffection had become as opposite poles of attraction that now served only to focus the attention of the unseen bitterness around them.

The weight of sensibility, so lightly worn by Douglas, was now to be carried by my son. The burden of two shouldered by one was not altogether accepted without a struggle, but without recourse to other ways or kindred spirits, events were drawing to their inevitable conclusion.

*

The chill of inaction made him shiver and alerted him to the muffled sounds of Douglas's progression above. He leant into the gully, as far as he dared, to prepare himself to follow. There was no sign of his companion. The rope looked foolishly out of place without a visible means of support at the other end; its occasional twitching back into life amidst the constant shower of ice scuttling down the artery walls told him that the top had not yet been reached. He looked at the coils at his feet. Ten, maybe fifteen feet left. The possibility that there wasn't enough rope now brought him fully back to reality.

He made a guess.

'Ten foot left!' he shouted. 'Maybe more.' He tried not to sound too concerned.

'I'm nearly there … a few more feet that's all!' Douglas's words demanded his patience. 'Stand clear!'

The warning from Douglas preceded an upsurge in the disfiguration. Cascades of cleaved blocks of snow and ice chiselled out of the cornice above, flew down the gully, wailing like a siren as they tumbled past him. He tried to dull the noise by covering his ears with his hands, only to have the sound magnified in his head a thousand times as each one shattered on the rocks below.

'I'm through! Nearly there,' repeated Douglas.

Shortly afterward, as planned, Christian untied the rope and tossed the end of it into the gully for Douglas to pull up. The nakedness of standing free without restraint from above was both unnerving and liberating. He felt wretchedly detached from the desecration he was otherwise bound to in every way. He was alone but surrounded: impotent, barren, desolate, and forsaken amid destruction.

The reappearance of the rope, now with dancing staves attached, was faintly miraculous. After a good deal of stretching and some deft juggling by Douglas, he again found himself attached to his destiny. He released his hold and edged into the gully.

Instantly, he felt the chilling updraft tear at his clothes. He stiffened against the assault. The cold slapped his skin, bit hard into his lungs and stung his eyes. Blind. His first step ricocheted away from the foothold Douglas had cut and spun him off balance. Undone. A flailing staff exploded off the ice and out of his grip. Fallen. He arched pirouetting into the gully and across to the other side like a sack of corn strung from a hayloft.

'In God's name, what's happened?' Douglas cried, 'Find a hold ... quick!'

He kicked hard and grabbed at the black and white images crazily gyrating before him. He felt a bruising pain in his shoulder; spinning, he instinctively struck out and clung to the solid saviour. His world returned to the vertical as his legs shuddered into a boulder just below where he had been standing seconds earlier. He hauled himself back up to the ledge and closed his eyes. He rested on his knees, fighting for breath.

'I'm alright ... I'm alright,' he spluttered. 'Wait ... give me a moment.'

Slowly, he straightened up. He felt as if a horse had kicked him in the stomach, and his shoulder was numb. I've lost a staff ... I've lost a staff, he half-choked, half-whispered to himself, as though the fatal realisation would be lessened by the repeated admission. He breathed deeply.

'I've dropped a staff.'

This time the confession mockingly echoed heaven-wards. He wasn't going to wait for an answer.

'You'll have to keep the rope tight. Take in the slack.'

The reassuring tension on the rope encouraged him to the very limit of his ability. He stretched as far as he dared and sank the pick of his staff into the embattled ice, easing his foot into position and carefully extending the welcoming hold. One more move and he was off the ledge and pinned to the stairway. Prostrated. He closed his eyes and step by step tried to imagine the way ahead: broken images of a broken ladder leading to a desecrated house of heaven; Leeds, his father, his shattered dreams, the wrath of angels, his mother's sorrow – all whirled before him forcing him to abandon his vision. He chose instead to vent his anger and frustration on the frozen layers of tears. He struck hard into the white chill of the steely aisle he so desperately wanted to leave. Each successive strike and driven boot loosed ever more screeching shards to shower down upon him before scuttling and cackling their way down the slope below, spitting like a thousand serpents as they flew and spiralled in the teeth of the squall that was urging them up; up, back, back into the face of their slayer.

This cacophony of sounds was now attended by something of infinitely greater intent. The presence of unseen shadows that circled Christian earlier that morning had coalesced into an assembly that darkened even the luminescent brilliance of winter's purest covering. The buffeting and tearing hordes of vicious demon forces now frenziedly fought for the soul of Christian. The glory of Creation was the only witness.

His mind was numb with cold, his body exhausted; his imagination had no defences, no boundaries. Terror was his only companion. As a tide of insanity washed over him, unseen hands beckoned and cajoled him to surrender.

He shuddered as a foot slipped from safety. The countering arc of his staff swung in a grotesquely distorted curve towards the taut lifeline above. As time rested, he witnessed the severing of fading hope, the hemp strands peeling away as his blade carved into the rope, before rebounding off the ice to send him spinning, wickedly, into the gully wall. Forgiven. He took one final breath before the renewed tension applied by Douglas completed his work, releasing him into oblivion and freeing him from the torment of knowing the inevitability of his shortcomings. The spiralling descent and ragged puncture of his body has no place in a memory closed to such horrors by the grace of departing life.

The realisation of the end came in the exhalation of spirit and soul as Christian's body plummeted out of the gully towards the snow-covered rocks below. He was dead long before he reached the ground. The gully, which had earlier captured his mind and had just seconds before been the scene of such turmoil, was silent.

*

It started to snow. First the sun, then the hills faded from view; daylight followed, until only the silent, falling angels remained.

Christian's Story

Beyond Time

I RELIVE THE FOLLOWING passage with the absolute horror that can only accompany the realisation of my death. Despite the fact that I now see it afresh, as one looking back in the knowledge and certainty of what has occurred, there is no lessening of the agony within me at the suddenness of the outcome. I was in no sense prepared for the rapid and conclusive separation of all that I had known, and for the complete and utter absence of perception and meaning that was to follow. All doubt, speculation and argument had been removed, giving clarity to a brutal truth: my life had come to its end.

*

As I raised my arm and swung the staff on that last occasion, not only did I know the pending outcome, but I also saw and heard the screeching, gaseous mass of foreign darkness riding against the intended point of delivery to steer the lightening white blade of my adze deep into the chords of rope above. The final cut in the pitch black of despair was not mine, but it was of my hand. For the briefest, cruellest moment of all, I hung between two worlds, only then to feel the terrible weight of one grotesque claw to release me from my lifeline. The rush of tearing clothes, the crack of limbs, the unforgiving flailing of flesh on stone mingled with my own last howls and distant cries from Douglas; all of which, in turn, was subsumed by a banshee-like wailing to give a trailing sound of fading life as I catapulted out of the confines of the gully. I knew, without pain, the single final blow, and fleetingly held the image of my dear mother bending over what remained of my earthly body on the fell below. As I faded from the pages of one world into another, her grief, entwined with my own anguish at being the cause of her sorrow, was etched into my final moment.

I saw and heard no more. From that moment on, my recollection is one of lasting stillness and suspense. I was blind in a darkness that was not of my making. No sun was lighted up, the world to view. I knew the sense of sight, but there was nothing to see and I had no means of seeing. I knew light without lustre and image without form. I was deaf in an eternal peace that covered and consumed me. I longed to cry out, but had no words to break a silence that had never known sound. I could listen, but there was no voice and I could not hear. I knew the sense of smell, the sweet joy of spring, and the taste of home-grown fruit, but no scent teased or flavour stirred my hunger. I could not pierce my surroundings in any way to discover where I was or what I might be. I was lost in an unworldly wilderness. I wanted to reach out, but had no feeling or means of touch to know whether I was whole. I was confined in a desert of meaning. I was in the most sterile of places in the most wanting of worlds.

The absence of pain or any sense of physical discomfort or need neither alarmed nor eased my position. I accepted the end of all that I had known with a calmness that came with the certainty that I was without form or identity: no more that which I had been, but instead something that I was waiting to know and become. The place I was in was thus known to me only by what it was not. It was as blank a canvas as could ever be imagined, with as black a palette from all eternity of darkness as ever there was. Without question, the poor artist, were he to find himself in such a place, could only aspire to become a part of some unfathomably dark, but unquestionably greater picture.

Without such companions to life, that I once so casually relied upon for all evidence of reality, I was left with no means to describe something inexplicable to me. I gauged that I still existed, in some small part, as I retained a capacity to absorb that which was not; that in itself, I concluded, was something. But the overwhelming absence of all else was as final an end to all that I knew as life as I could imagine. It was, it seemed, the unalterable closure to all things done and all things to come in a world that I looked back on as having once thought so full of promise. All that I had held to be set out before me to await my rightful calling was to be left untouched and unfulfilled by my absence. What I was experiencing was unknown and far beyond my ability to know my shortcomings. I was without foundation, bereft of all sensible pillars of reason, and fading into a pit beyond the limits of conscionable boundaries.

This suspension, this vacuum, this maze of matchless unknowing was without charity or mercy. I had been cast aside from the fullness and pleasures of a physical world to be in a place that, to my comprehension, was without character or charm. There was, after all, no end to existence. Instead, there was to be solitude within which to reflect upon loss and unfulfilment. All that had been left undone and unspoken would now be my legacy of missed opportunities, and worse, the hopes of one who had invested so much in the life of another would be forever crushed.

Mourning for life – if that is what had taken hold of me – was not some inner reflection of loss alone, nor was it pity for empty promise, or shame for word or deed left undone; its boundary did not even rest at the limits of my mother's despair. There was a dullness that consumed regret, to the extent that life itself had been cast as nothing but a token of inconsequence to a greater unknown. All its worldly aspirations had been futile and foolish. All that I had understood, and all that I had believed to belong to the essence of my being, had been swept aside to be replaced with fallacy and doubt. The absence of knowledge or reason, of truth or meaning, or the faintest indication as to my situation was now my consuming entitlement. I had become detached from freedom by the evaporation of thought and suppression of will to resist a greater command to let go. The confinement of my situation was isolating me from resistance, and as the barriers closed in upon me I felt myself sink into a haze of deceit and half-truths. Half-dead, half-unborn, and trapped between suffering and submission, I could not let go and I could not hold on. I was lost to all that was known, in a place far removed from memory.

*

The horror of meaninglessness isolates the mind from sane counsel and reasonable judgement. The loss of association with any substantial matter of consequence separates minded conclusion from the turmoil of madness. This alone is enough to release the mind from its struggle to decipher the mysteries of a familiar world, let alone the unintelligible secrets of a greater unknown. This was the poorest of all possible circumstance: to be without relation to any other can only be likened to the impossibility of consciousness without body or soul.

*

How long I dwelt on such crazed persuasions of reality I cannot say, but so bleak was my position that the void about me was irreducible fear. No dressing stemmed the flow; no argument or wild sophistry of the mind stayed the loss of hope from my mood; I was simply alone and isolated from reason.

It is of no wonder that, bereft of perception and cast adrift from any notion of account for my situation, I should sink into the numbness of oblivion. What is to astound, is that at some point I did return – not to madness of a kind that denies all expression, or to the bewilderment of a lost soul as to how I might exist without evidence of existence, but to emptiness.

Without this unwilful suppression of consciousness, I'm sure I would have succumbed to a deranged illusion of reality. Perhaps, I would have lost forever that faculty that directs, comforts, and so leads a being to believe in itself. That I did not fall is evidence enough, even at this early stage of my experience, that I had become something other than before.

*

The human mind does not exist in isolation and never has. The loss of consciousness was not a loss but a revelation – the discovery of an 'un-minded' part that lies within to guide the infant in its wanderings through the mindful world. The search for order and meaning is not at the sole behest of humankind. Long before life, there was an authority that strove to balance the competing demands of freedom with the freedom to deny authority.

*

And so it was that I settled into that suspension between the known and the unknown with a degree of resignation that I was powerless to resist. All that I knew came to me without enquiry and without the luxury of exploration –

and was nothing. All that I did not know was much more and required me to shed all that I held to be true of life before moving on to some new notion of existence.

Discovery

I T SEEMED AS THOUGH my mind was all I had ever been, for if not that, then what else determines the self to all others about it? What else places each one of us in such a way as to make it seem that the centre of all creation is focused upon our view of it?

No other matters. No other offers an alternative to be concerned with.

What is and what is not, is known solely by its bearing upon the eye of the beholder. And now, without that last vestige of self to search and uncover an order of relationship to anything else, what had I become, if not some immortal transport of being? If not of mind, then I was, I concluded, as nothing.

To relate this change from life to some new form of being as a transition is not the sole extent of my experience. It is, in truth, a part – a significant part, but by no means all that must now be grasped as accounting for my distress. I was, I believe, undergoing more a sequence of separations from one set of beliefs and values cast in one world to a completely new perspective on existence in another. I was in another place, invisible and unknown to physical senses, whilst clinging to thoughts and memories that were nothing but sensory dust hidden in the folds of time.

Such prime elements of life as I had known in the physical world were of no help to me now. I had become something anew without shedding the entirety of what I once was; it was this attachment, this thread to the past, that was to become so crucial in what was to unfold.

My mind – for that is how I still regard my being – retained impressions of my mortal condition. I had, after all, drawn comparisons with orphaned senses to seek some sort of release from their absence. However, as an entity capable of thought alone, I retained a function of memory and the ability to regret, but without external signals to draw upon, without sensory perceptions to indulge the imagination, without experience or hitherto knowledge of my situation. Without all this, I was unable to come to any sensible conclusion as to the form to which I belonged. It was this alienation from all before and all around me that drove me to such despair and helplessness. I existed as a mind torn between what I had known as reality and something that now contradicted everything I had ever believed or thought possible.

It was this travesty, this denial of what was beyond the comprehension of my mortal mind, that closed in upon me and constrained me so. This wretched assault on the sensitivity and breadth of a single view of existence had come to declare nothing more or less than the dying exertions of life to assign truth to that, alone, which can be conceived.

The world I believed in, the world of physical beings and tangible matter, was full of evidential truths and notional concepts, but nothing real or imaginary could have prepared me for the loss of my identity whilst still retaining some knowledge of it.

A physical being embodies the essence of life: the interpretation of stimuli, the conscious deliberations and judgements that allow freedom of choice, the emotions, the recall of knowledge and the accumulation of wisdom; all of this proclaims life. It would be true to say that I retained some remnant of this condition. I was able to recall what it was that I had lost, and I was able to indulge in reason of a kind, albeit one that excluded understanding, but – and this is the nub of the matter – it was unfounded; it was without belief, without surround; it was without the physical girdle that embraces life. I had been starved of all that enabled me to believe in the verity of my situation.

I had become inconceivable to Truth.

I now bridged a divide between beliefs (which become embedded in the human psyche), and unsupported imaginings (which do not). It is the body that belongs to the physical world. It comes from matter and remains with it; thus it is confined and condemned to live in one world, with a single view of it. What comes after – the possibility of there being more to life – cannot be accounted for by the conscious mind.

Wondrous as it is, the physical form is no more than the most basic vehicle for a greater archive of being; the body is the visible print of an invisible presence. It is a shuttered window, a shimmering horizon, a dusty manuscript, but one that rarely permits sight of its inner-chronicler. On one level, the outer-self, with its mindful preoccupations, is recognised by its manner and deeds; its ways and habits are ascribed characteristics, which in turn define and enforce the nature of the physical form and differentiate it from all other; on another level, the inner-being is the unannounced resolve or the unexpected restraint on a familiar course that goes against all reason and becomes the exception to the rule of its kind. What is known comes from the past and is engrained in life as the light of experience; what is unknown remains as a seed, a legacy of long-forgotten beginnings to be carried forward in darkness. The selfish mind does not exist alone; there is another energy not subject to the same laws as the body that accompanies it. I had become this new thing, this unconscionable presence or ethereal stream of consciousness – its naming is less important than its being.

It was this other self that I denied. I denied it because I did not know it and could not conceive it. What I had known was left behind for me to lament; what I could not know I carried with me in ignorance. What appeared to be isolated from all that I could believe was, in fact, the only thing that could reconcile the past with the present and lead me to the future.

Physical powers alone are insufficient to decipher the mysteries of two worlds. I failed to understand, or could not accept this, and so was left in the darkness of a foolish mind.

*

When ignorant armies fight in the dark and foolish minds dual in the past, when every day becomes night, and all that is wrong is decreed right, therein lies the tyranny of reason.

The Monadic Form

I HAD BEEN PLACED in a world without colour, sound, aroma, or matter of any kind. A world without wonder or light, so free of substance, shape, or measure of time that it cannot be described in any meaningful way to verify its presence. Such darkness and weight of emptiness crushes all expectation of release and stifles free will. It is an oppression that denies the senses and shames an enquiring mind. If such a place could be teased at all onto the canvas of a lively imagination, it would be as a reflection of imprecision itself and as wrongful an image of durability as any castle of sand in the desert. And yet, here, now, before me lay that question: how in all eternity of castle-building could such an image be grasped?

*

In truth, the riddle is only part told, for in addition to that so far described, there is one thing and one thing only that needs to be added. It is a mantle that is itself the source of all being: the monadic presence that embraces all existence, no matter what or where that may be. Furthermore, that single entity is as broad in understanding of spiritual and mortal being, and as powerful a means for delivery of meaning to life as anything that has ever been encountered, or could possibly be imagined from the confines of the shroud that encapsulates the physical mind.

This one indivisible, simplicity of being is all that is required for all else to be.

There is no shape or size to this encircling might. It must be recognised in the same way that a feeling or emotion arises from within, expressing all that cannot be seen or described. It exists as fear, as hope, as love, as sorrow; it is as all emotions are in the physical world, as expressions that are granted to – but extend beyond – human beings to touch and declare as belonging to their world. The source of such a power that intrudes upon the comforts of mortal life is rarely dwelt upon; it may appear as a play upon the mind or come from within as a shadow to evoke some deep regret at careless words or deeds; it may encroach upon sadness to comfort, or call to arms to right injustice.

Above all else, it is the character, the unfashioned and unframed essence of being.

It is the first before all else can be. Without it, there can be no emotion and no life. Being is a pre-condition to life, and so it is with the monadic entity as a pre-condition to being.

Before life, this was all there was: the spirit of unspoken wonders and unheralded imaginings. It is the harbour outside the physical world that shelters all spirits and unseen energies; it is a world beyond words. But if a world requires hard evidence of its existence, then it is not a world that will be seen, for no physical senses will ever come to rest here.

This place, so loosely alluded to as a world, has no pretence or loyalty to worldly reality: so constrained, so sheltered is life as to accept only that which can be seen, or to believe only that which can be subscribed to without doubt. The resolve to seek enlightenment through the pursuit of evidence and to measure all wisdom by the past is crippling to the attainment of understanding. Faith and trust are necessary to believe. Faith in the destiny of the mind – freed from its ties to the physical form – and trust in the course of eternity to come to rest in a place of quiet acquiescence to the decree of a higher authority.

Only then can the veil be lifted to reveal the presence of another place.

The concept of a non-physical world may barely be grasped, even as the most fleeting of introductions to a notion beyond the comprehension of most normal powers of imagination. Alone, such limits of insight would justifiably preclude acceptance of such a suggestion; furthermore, add the constraints of paucity of expression and dullness of experience, and any sensible mind would most certainly struggle to retain for a moment the briefest vision of the beauty and simplicity that comes from the fullest level of comprehension.

As awe-inspiring as the most opulent, colourful vista and splendour of form in shape and texture of natural spectacle may be in the physical world, so, conversely, may be the most basic and simplest realisation of the non-physical world. For one, the art is in seeing and knowing through the physical senses, and in the other it is the embracing of all possible fullness to expand belief through unseen dimensions to achieve understanding of the role of all things.

The combination of knowledge and understanding within the fuller embodiment of both is to position the physical and metaphysical worlds inside this greater monadic entity.

If the notion of another world may be painful to consider in a frame of reference that is bound so much by witness that disbelief becomes a barrier to progression, then accept that physical being will never enter this other place. Reflect not on what constitutes this place, but on where it is. As with anything that is taxing to define, it can be rewarding to state that which it is not, so as to remove false idols before focusing on the faintest imagery to convey further the concept offered.

No affinity to above, below or beyond the physical world is appropriate, as discovery is not dependent upon positioning that which *is* in proximity to that which has only been adjudicated to *be*. That is not to say the physical world is not real, rather that it has only been made to appear the sum of all reality in the absence of any other testimony. Witness is not the sole arbitrator of truth. This other world cannot be seen in terms of past, present or future, as there is no concept of time in a place where matter does not exist.

What is sought is beyond the boundaries of what is

known – it has, though, always been inside the realm of supposition. That is the dichotomy facing the mind.

On the one hand, there is knowledge, and on the other, there is a notion. When the two coincide, there is harmony in understanding, but when the two are in opposition there is conflict and uncertainty. If knowing and believing were at all times in all things as one, then comprehension would be universal and assured. If knowledge equates to the physical world – seeing, touching and hearing – and belief equates to the metaphysical world – trust, faith and conviction – then the two may be seen as two distinct facets of the same entity, residing within one body.

The concept of knowledge and belief existing within a single form illustrates how the metaphysical and physical worlds come together *within* the greater monadic presence of existence. This 'other world' is all around and within all matter. Physical and metaphysical worlds are collocated and, in the case of the physical world, it is a cohabited environ of the body on the one hand and unseen metaphysical forces on the other. The primary distinction between the two places is one of occupancy, not location.

The Creator becomes the created, becomes the Creator.

*

It was from within this new dimension that I came to a point of submission. Such an air as follows a storm, when all elements are resting to reflect on their doing, settled upon my being. It was an eye of stillness, a silent acknowledgement of the futility of struggle against an insuperable weight of reason. A more peaceful dawn had broken and quelled the misgivings of a forsaken mind; I felt a newborn acceptance – if not yet of reason, then of graceful reasonability.

I welcomed the respite from the preceding turmoil, and the fresh hope that had come to answer the questions I hadn't had the wherewithal to ask – or the knowledge to know needed asking. I knew no hunger or physical need. I could discern no change to my surroundings or appreciation of my existence, but I was resigned to reflect anew on my position. I had become childlike in my readiness to absorb my suffering afresh in the hope of attention and recognition of my plight. What had been most distressing to me had passed, and my horizon was lighter because of it.

The past, for all I knew, had never been a part of my present. If I had awoken, then perhaps it was from a dream. Perhaps, I was still awakening and the truth of my position was awaiting my return, as the wanderings of a fanciful mind might return to acknowledge the unreasonableness of its behaviour.

I had a sense of change within me as I began to open up to what could be, instead of what was not. I knew there was no light, but I perceived an impression of clarity. I could catch the faintest glimmer of meaning and purpose to my presence as the bright lights of worldly callings faded to the clear canvas of a new beginning. There was no sound, but I had a voice within that reflected my thoughts and I could acquire understanding by absorbing such truths as were embedded around me in my isolation. All of this combined to present me with the most basic vision of what I now felt myself to be. Above all else, I had a continuance and a wholeness of thought. I had knowledge without expectation or desire to benefit from it, and I had begun to reach beyond the limits of my attachment to the physical senses. I was none the wiser as to my position or indeed what form I took, but I accepted that it was not as flesh that relied upon care and nurture to survive.

It is not possible to say how long acceptance of my position took, as time has no part in this other world. However, as a measure of recording events past or passing and in placing such events in sequence, time is a valid and just parameter to use in the chronicling of change in the closed physical world. It is only when one leaves that world of mere physical senses that time becomes an unreliable chronicler for all that takes place in its name. So it is that I am unable to say how long my experiences lasted, either as a distinct event or as part of the greater story. Suffice to say that my recollections are continuous and lasting.

*

The concept of time is important to understand the difference between all forms of life in the physical world and all phases of existence in this other world. It records the passing of light to dark and the growth of young to old. It is also true that this would continue without time as its chronicler.

From a world with time, a moment or a millennium in a world without it is as nothing as what occurs in its name is unknown by the hands that refute all outside of their sweep. Time may record the passing of days and the coming of the end to life, but it doesn't record what cannot be grasped as endless. Those that live by its hands, move on without understanding what they have missed. Time exists only for that which falls under its reach, and it lasts only as long as each object, or event, remains visible to its pulse, but in the absence of either there is no need or means of assigning a measure to such tokens from the physical world.

Time distinguishes between what can be known and what cannot. This simple truth is central to the acknowledgement of the possibility that the absence of time does not preclude the sharing between two worlds of what takes place in its name – worlds that exist as collocated environs of the same space.

This duality of existence between the temporal and non-temporal worlds allows the cohabitation of the physical world, by the unbodied, to be undertaken within the physical form. Whilst gathered this way, the body-spirit adheres to the same laws and rhythms of time as the physical being. When not gathered, the spirit is free and not bound by the same rules of time.

The effect is to allow the present, when seen from the physical world, to be overlaid with the past or future when viewed from the spiritual world. This insight may be shared between gathered and ungathered spirits and thereby be made known to the physical mind. Such visitations from the past or premonitions of a future are not unusual.

It was just such a scenario that Christian experienced

in the valley that morning on the way up to Dale Head. He was confronted with the spectre of his father turning back down the hill to return home prior to his death. The past had been summoned in this way to forestall the path he was on and had he responded in such a way as to change his course then the day's outcome would have been different.

The conscious mind is as much a party to reality as it is an observer of it. At the moment of decision, the freedom to choose determines reality and forestalls all other variants of it. This capture of a moment in time is continuously enacted, affecting the next and all subsequent moments and the freedom granted to choose at each one. But freedom has a cost. What has passed cannot be undone, and just as Christian chose to ignore the presence of his father and continue to travel to each new end, so the spectre of inevitability loomed over him until he became so constrained that the final outcome was as much of his own making as it was of the darkness about him.

The death of Christian was not part of any great plan. It was neither inevitable nor, in the final moments, preventable, given the circumstances and the outcome of each of a series of events that in themselves were small steps on one of many alternative paths through life. The outcome at each turn and each crossroad was not the prerogative of some higher authority, nor was it the result of chance – as though by the toss of a fateful coin by some passing maverick. It was simply the result of freedom.

What took place in the gully was the result of not one

but many previous occasions of choice, most of which Christian was not even a party to. But, ultimately, it was he who was in a position whereby all preceding acts had come to a point from which there was no escape; a point where the myriad of intricacies and plays upon plays, that impose a hidden hand on life, was indelibly cast in matter as a record to be exposed in the final account.

The journey may be short or long, simple or complex, but it is always influenced by that from which it started. Such strings that thread a way through time are, when unravelled in the world without time, revealed as a closure on just one part of a greater reality. They are words on a page, within a chapter, within a book that is there for all to read, but which can never be completed as the final act will also see the end of the book itself.

As it transpired, Christian was blind to the warnings he received. The agitation of his mind, the labour of his step, and the spectre of his father all passed unattended. His mind was also closed to the less subtle signs: the stillness that precedes danger, as those mortal creatures with higher senses give way to the tread of more powerful forces, the shadows that dulled his mind, and the fleeting, vaporous loss and reconnection of spiritual awareness. All these alarms passed him by.

He carried an increasing burden of denial through self-doubt that left a trail of growing despair and negative energy. This became a scent of weakness that culminated in the coalition of forces that prey on frailties of this nature. The absence of any distraction for these assassins and the lack of harbour, or will, to retreat from inhospitable surroundings, all added to the threat and air of inevitability on the journey. These forces were powerful in number, effect, and choice of location. Not only were Christian's options limited in the confines of the gully, but so too was his recourse to aid. The physical surrounds were in favour of a collective malevolent will and against the limitations of the human body and spirit. What took place was an unequal battle of wills from different worlds, one unconstrained and the other shackled by an unimpeachable commandment to sustain life and maintain harmony and balance between all things.

At the very last, when no other recourse remains, the moment of death is the outcome of spirit and soul leaving the body.

At this point, the physical being no longer exists. The body is a shell that remains in isolation from the final reality. Absent from further part, its mortal works are engrained in the past as a monument to life's inability to exceed its mother source. That life has its origin in something greater than itself, something more powerful, more knowing and more durable, is all that can be asserted without contradiction. To do otherwise would be to deny its continuance.

Regression

IT WAS FROM THIS place of stillness and acceptance of a wider reality that I began to acquire the essence of being. The monadic form, which I came to know as always having been the authority for existence, had entered my consciousness and now held me so completely that it suppressed my wilful need to question my situation. I was certainly no longer alone and of free mind. Although I felt no fear, I was conscious of a binding presence upon all that I was and would become. I had been consumed by an external will that left me without freedom to resist. There was no voice or vision, just an overwhelming internal commitment to an authority in whose power I was now employed. As my will submitted to obedient acceptance so I felt all things within me slow to a new pulse. The hasty judgements, unfounded doubts and fears, faded in the face of a dawning recognition that there was, after all, something – a presence, maybe, or an influence – to which an attachment or duty continued.

If such counsel as would allay the tremors of hasty judgement were ever needed, then it must be now, for after all that I have told so far, there comes a turn: a twist, a moment's regression, or worse – a deception, not just in time, but in the sentiment that regards the indivisibility of truth as beyond contemplation.

*

I recall no surprise at becoming aware of increasing light and familiar surroundings as I came upon my crumpled body on the white bed of snow beneath me. The still falling flakes had not yet faded the outline, and the lifeless form seemed a rare intrusion upon winter's shroud.

My discovery seemed as natural as awakening from a dream. As the fading vestiges of sleep drain from an awakening child, so I felt the last ties of my earthly existence once more seep from me to give comfort and assurance to a dazed mind that it had indeed passed this way before. I was reminded that what had been was not an end to all things, but merely a passing, a freedom and freshness to welcome the onset of a new beginning. I had no thought that I was returning to relive the past or to cast judgement upon it, but I was sure that what had befallen my mortal being was engrained within me. Just as a dream might play upon a mind at rest, so was I now witnessing, from afar, the scenes that evaded my physical self.

As I so easily held my last earthly memories before me, a faint echo of my name filtered into my consciousness. It was Douglas kneeling on a pulverised platform of snow and peering over the precipice in desperation as he hauled in the last few feet of rope. His anguished cries were broken with calls for God's forgiveness and pleas for help and restoration. In all my sorrow I had not known such despair and with all that remained within me I reached out to arrest his tortured lament.

I had no voice, but I felt words leave me as a thought passes from memory – lost to the wind rather than deliberately cast on its way. It was as though I embraced and held his pain within the palm of my being. I sought to calm his horror and relieve his self-reproach by calling his name and imploring him not to persecute himself so.

The effect was as a blow unseen, a bolt unleashed upon an unsuspecting mind, a knife turned in an already smarting wound. I had no expectation that I could ever again communicate with another being, and certainly not by the power of will as I now appeared to have done. Douglas had not only heard but was looking straight at me. His recoil from despair to disbelief was lightning in effect. I could sense the fear invading his body. I sought again to allay the distress I had caused with the thought that, although I was no more in his world, I was safe, at rest, and he should not blame himself. He looked about in the chill terror of uncomprehending despair, as though seeking what was already there in front of him but unreachable in his mind. He scrambled to his feet and dropped the end of the shredded rope back into the gully. He turned once, twice, spinning in a vortex of doubt and dread, before scampering, sliding, and tumbling down the hill in the direction of the route to the valley below. It was then that I knew – as I had done earlier that day – he had heard but not truly seen. My earlier impression that I could commune at will was flawed.

*

For a while, I was lost, beset by grief from the world that I had once embraced as all that I could ever need or know. All that had befallen this day in the name of life had occurred amid great beauty and there seemed no account for it. I could not but question my part in this tragic drama, so innocently conceived, but now so complex with so many unscripted intrusions; surely, the playwright would be rendered aghast at the effect of his words on the beleaguered actors. What hand lay so harshly on this page to bring such tragedy to minor players when all else seemed so touched with perfection?

If such questions had a rightful place within drama, then I knew that they were to be left without answers in life. I had been bound with a pledge of understanding to hold on to a lifeline of greater reason in exchange for my sanity, but now as I drifted into the mire of doubt between good intention and bold undertaking, the strain of one reality was lost to a mirage of another. I was compelled to linger and struggle with all that could not be explained in the language of life.

From my unworldly vantage point, I missed nothing of the tableau before me. From the peaks to the valleys I read and witnessed all that had ever been, as though the pages of this place were laid out before me. I was part of an unfolding pageant of scenes and scenery, of play upon play, of actors and acts, of bedazzling and bewitching entertainment each contributing to the drama. All that took place in the name of creation was there before me to wonder at and, yes, to question. As I witnessed one world, I knew of another – that in itself was light. The two were apart, broken, lost to the other in some pitiful tragedy of circumstance that bore into the very soul of reason calling for mercy. What work had first divided man from his Maker was beyond my understanding, but that the two were once one was as clear to me as the knowledge of my continued part in this play.

My questions came from ignorance and were foolish when set against my commitment to trust – at what point in the age of understanding had the mind ever become trustworthy? At what time did it look outside of its own experience to grasp that which it sought? What was it that created the object that so readily reveals the nature of all else as occasions of chance? If chance be all, then all is chance, and understanding is nothing more than whimsy. I had no right to question.

Homespun Warmth

A S MUST BE WITH all discoveries, the moment passed.
I was left with just a glimpse of what might be behind
the mystery that still evaded my questioning. Although
I had been shown something of the truth of what had
befallen me, I lacked far more than I knew. I didn't have
the conviction of my education to cast off my anxieties. In
all that I had learnt, I had no moment of revelation that
could stay my doubt, and I could not accept the call to
leave behind the yearning that bound me so tightly to the
past.

This was my dilemma: trust in the perception of no
more than might be revealed by the flicker of a dying
candle in the dead of night, or bow to a lineage so strong
as to overrule all shadowy intruders in favour of that
which can be held in the palm of the hand or fixed firm in
the eye of its beholder.

If choice it was that I had come to, then what was to
follow would be of my own making. I could not deny the
desire to explore the unknown, but neither could I pass
by the suffering I had witnessed and remain at ease. If I

had learnt anything so far, it was that there would be a consequence to my election, a reckoning that would rest in my character for as long as I retained the notion of life. I thus came to a settlement of mind that would tear me from my bonds and set me loose on ways the consequences of which I could not foresee.

I required the full disclosure of reason for all that had occurred on my last day of life. There were to be no exclusions, no lessening of the pain that comes from knowing one's full part in this act.

*

I was led deep into the dark, twisted territory of desire to have laid bare before me such barriers to liberty and choice as I had never faced before. I realised that if I were to be free of doubt, I had to oppose these guardians of truth and to peel away all that concealed my ambitions. All the charades of the mind which disguised personal achievement as worthy, and self-gain as profitable were to be confronted and examined. One by one I viewed and rejected each argument for just endeavour, each claim for righteous deed, and each appeal for generous thought, as wistful illusions of reality. Until, at last, at the very foundation of motive, I found only the basest tenet of self-glorification. The insatiable appetite for praise to satisfy a misconstrued notion of inner worth had only succeeded in alienating me from the simple pleasure I sought.

The crux of the day's tragedy was my blind faith in false judgements and flawed beliefs. In all that I uncovered, I was only to find emptiness and regret at not having heeded the many warnings placed before me. The clarity with which I now saw the pleasure of beauty untouched and nature unchanged was painful to bear when set against the honest labour and selfless toil of my parents. The whole tenor of their life – to work with their allotted hand – was in tune with the gifts and rhythms of all about them. Theirs was a song against my wailing, a light against my darkness, a palm against my fist. I had not heeded their ways or considered their needs above those of my own. I had succeeded only in destroying all that was so lovingly created and freely given.

And now, with all undone and set before me, the folly of my ways was hard upon me. I longed for it to be otherwise. Even now it seemed that I might deny the truth of it and settle for a lighter touch to ease my mind. But there was only one course open to me if I were to appease my conscience and atone for my scant regard to all that had been so carefully placed before me.

*

I had made my choice and, as before, I found myself attending my mortal body in the snow. However, this time there was not the assuredness of the past in my mind. What I confronted was as unlikely a confusion of hope and dread as could ever be mistaken for some future possibility. I came to the certain form of my dear mother, but as sure as I was of her presence, she was in the most unlikely surroundings. The mountains belonged to a world that I had held as my own, as far removed from her ways as I could conceive – and yet, this was the apparition I held: her back bowed, her arms reaching out over my crumpled body, her palms cradling my head. It was as an act of release and a final utterance of forgiveness. But it was also a moment of false witness, for it quickly faded and I knew that this time had not yet come and indeed might never come to pass in such a way.

No sooner had this vision left me then another followed. My mother was now in the comfortable surroundings of the parlour at Freeland, with all the warmth of homespun memories replacing the cold of the winter fells. The intensity of the eye was such that I could so easily have reached out to touch her as she swept back her dark hair to frame the russet roundness of her face in the glow of the firelight. As she made her preparations for the cold and concerned herself with the final touches to her hair, the layered folds of her black linen dress – in which I used to smother my anxieties as a child – busied and flowed around her like a beck in full spate. Her dark plaid cloak concealed the only vestige of white about her: 'the finest of all French lace apparel', as she used to say with mock indignation when pressed by my father to let him replace his first gift to her – now her most treasured possession. I wondered what comfort she would cling to when news of my death reached her this day.

Her deliberate routine and familiar bustle of dressing was accompanied, as always, by a silent entreaty to join in as she half-sang, half-hummed her favourite psalm.

I have no need, from Thee comes all,
Sheep of thy fold, or calves from thy stall;
For all the beasts within the woods,
Upon a thousand hills thy goods,
Hm ... hmm ... hm ... hmm ...
from thee comes all,
All birds which fly above the mountains' heights,
All fowl which play the fields and fountains' white;
Hm ... hmm ... .hm ... hmm ...
from thee comes all.

I was back in the parlour, waiting impatiently, breathing in the aroma of honey and rose-petal oil, and feasting upon the sounds of her voice whilst she readied herself for the Sunday gathering.

So far removed from all sadness was the scene, that the thought of her sorrow to be was an unwelcome intrusion when it finally came upon me. That I should be the cause of her grief was a pain I had carried ever since the moment of my departure from this world, and it now came to the fore as she moved back and forth amidst the intimate possessions of family life. I witnessed the joy of love as she let her fingers linger and her mind dwell on the pleasures recalled from gifts and tokens of my father's time. When the moment came, I dared to hope that she would come to loiter and draw comfort from familiar objects not yet free of my touch. I felt sure she would be bolstered by our shared memories and sentiments to fill the hours of darkness with reflections of lighter moments. Yet, much as I could everlastingly consume the images of my affection, I had no wish to dwell further on her sorrow to come.

I knew that my mother had not yet come to the time of my death, but as my attention turned again to the scene before me, I sensed my presence in that room had not passed unrecorded. A mist now covered my vision, so that the image I held was blanched and fading. I became enveloped in a certainty that she would come to be watched over by one close to guide and ease her through the coming news. How I came to this reassurance, I do not know, but I knew that I had freely given my thoughts and something of my belief that all was not yet done, in a way that would be held in the surrounds of my home long after this day had passed from memory.

The last I recall was her making that final, non-essential adjustment to the angle of her bonnet before taking her prayer books from the mantle-shelf, tucking them deep into the folds of her muff, and making her way to the door. Pausing, she took one last enquiring look about the room before making her way out into the yard.

As she left, so the images around me faded. My vision had been her gift and the memories that came from it my treasures. I had been blessed with a moment in time to return a token of comfort to her inner spirit: a truth that all was not lost and that what is taken from one world can be found in another in greater measure. I had given of myself in order that she would be fortified when the news of my death came to her.

I had dwelt in the past and lapped at the limits of two worlds to know the frailties of mind from one and the uncertainties of spirit from another. I was as yet of neither one nor the other.

The Third Way

M<small>Y THIRST FOR UNDERSTANDING</small> was a legacy from Creation itself. My right to know was as a heartbeat in time and a barrier to the enormity of such an undertaking. I know that I absorb experiences and reflect on what I have become. I know too that I have transcended the limits of mortal reach beyond touch and time.

After all I had been through since my death, I had known Douglas and my mother in the moment after my passing. Time had no influence on my continued existence. The concept of time as a step-by-step progression through change has always denied the possibility of ever returning to that which has passed. Now, it also denied the possibility of what takes place in the name of time from being shared across more than one world.

*

Just as there are two worlds, so must there be two different sized steps through change in each. In the physical world, each step is seen as the smallest possible movement –

or change – in an event, but as time is not known to *all* things, that smallest possible movement must also be defined by a common denominator if it is to be accepted that what takes place in the name of time must take place to all things – living or otherwise. The notation must be stated as that one step in which change occurs, regardless of the magnitude, pace, or knowledge of its occurrence.

This convention makes no call upon time. It makes no mention of measurement, either by rate or scale. It, therefore, allows a mechanism for understanding the progression and passage through events in both worlds without specifying the observable rate, sequence, or magnitude of change in those events. And it does not deny the possibility that change may occur simultaneously at the same point in two different worlds.

In the non-physical world, the step-by-step passage of events has no place or necessity. There is no distinction between the passing from night to day, or young to old as neither cycle is necessary where dark and light, and birth and death have no say. There are no objects, no borders or limits, and no contrast between the past and future. However, this place does not exist in isolation, and so it is necessary to visualise that which takes place in the timeless, non-physical world requires a different order from that which takes place in the time-full, physical world.

Imagine the impossible image of two human beings occupying the very same space at the same time. One is very young and one is very old. One sees everything around him for the first time without knowledge or experience to influence his judgement; the other sees the past in everything before him and imagines the future for his companion. Both use the same physical senses, but both see things differently. That in itself is a discord. Now add the fact that both are constrained by the limitations of physical senses, and you add dullness and paucity – an absence of fullness – to discord. The only flaw in this image, of course, is that two human beings cannot occupy the same space at the same time.

But ... what if one was not of a physical nature?

*

It was through this denouncement of time that I became infused with a new comprehension of being.

The separation of my spiritual self from my physical self had a part to play in my passing from one world to the next, but it would also be necessary to free my consciousness in readiness to accept my spiritual rejuvenation.

That dark period I spent in suspension following the passing of mortal life, takes place at a crossing linking the two worlds – an island free of all obligation and expectation. It is a release from the physical body to allow the spirit to rest and dwell on its role before returning to the world from whence it came.

That third place is not in itself a world. It has no enduring characteristics. It has no permanence beyond that which is necessary to allow a spirit to pass through on its journey from life. It may be thought of as a gateway, but only insofar as it allows the passage from one place to another. A gateway does not provide shelter nor does it overlap – in the sense that it contains something of the two parts it divides.

Besides offering a thoroughfare between two worlds, this third place allows characteristics of each to exist whilst the passage is completed; once a spirit has passed through, it is closed and all that has been discarded is lost from spiritual memory forever.

It is here, too, that time rests. There is no ordering of the past or appointing of the future to interfere with the uncoupling of all that was held as real and conclusive in life. A spirit is alone in a vacuum: a conscience of worldly frailties. Memories of life – embracing time – remain encapsulated in spiritual reason whilst a spirit is in the third place.

Thus came my spiritual mind to this third place – filled with the bounty of the past and all the adornments that come with a mortal lifetime to hold in trust for an unmeasured now, until I was ready to move on with knowledge of the part I played in one short moment of existence.

This coming together as two forms in a single expression to share a common point is a powerful glimpse of the enormity of existence. The physical 'I' remains as a series of memories centred on the self. All observations, emotions, and beliefs have come from within and are retained as images of internal values projected onto external events. The spiritual 'I' holds all these memories but surrounds them with much more. It is this detailed and fuller understanding that enables a spirit not just to relive a moment, as in the recall of an image of reality from memory, but to replay the fullness of reality itself. It places the image within a greater view, which, in turn, places an event in context of sense and reason, rather than in time alone.

To gauge the enormity of the gulf between the physical 'I' centred observation and the spiritually omnipotent 'I' awareness, consider the simple movement of placing one foot in front of the other. The foot moves, displacing the air and the snow as it passes by. It comes to rest in a new place, thereby creating a fresh appearance to the external arrangement of things. A change to something small also changes something large.

All this most delicate disturbance to air, earth, and stone is captured by the spirit and relayed – together with the general observations of the less sensitive physical being – to the soul as a record. It is this extra sense – of a step taken through all elements and the effect it has on the wider reality of the moment – which enables a spirit to recall the event, the emotion, and reason for the change in the picture.

There is no need to judge the paucity of one view against the richness of the other. All that is required is an appreciation of a moment in life when set against the fullness of the reason for that moment in existence.

The spiritual 'I' is an encyclopaedic discourse on a life with all its mortal fears, frailties, indulgences, and endeavours. Nothing is omitted and nothing is judged. It is a labour of care and devotion to life.

Whilst it is the soul that retains the record of life, it is a spirit that captures all else, and on departing from life, it is a spirit that has to disclose and atone for its part. To do this it must first shed its attachment to the centred view and memories of physical life. This it does in the third place. This has always been the way – until now.

To understand more, it is necessary to reveal that not only does the third place link the physical with the non-physical world, but it also shares the same space with both until the passage from one to the other has been completed. The dynamics of events in this third place will differ in content from the other two, being as it is, a fusion of both time and non-time-based worlds; however, the three spaces are anchored at the point of departure from life to allow completion of the transition.

As my spirit left my mortal body so it came to rest in suspension between the physical and spiritual worlds. Do not think of this as one spirit in two places at the same time, but as one spirit in-between two worlds, aware of both and absorbing something from each.

This, though, is where my declaration falters and my assurance as to the veracity of my understanding fades. It is clear that I did not complete that transition from one world to the next. I, as spirit, had failed to leave the physical world, and I failed to shed my attachment to it.

Thus, it was my spirit that, freed from the notion of time, gazed upon my body. All the many deliberations I entered into whilst in this third place were as nothing in time in the physical world. Having looked back and relived my last moment of life, I should have resigned myself to the way of it before continuing my journey on to the spiritual world. Instead, I dallied with friendship to console, and toyed with love to comfort; both of which I now know endangered those I sought to give succour. The calling of my name came not, as I supposed, from Douglas – for I had no means to attend to such pleadings – but from his spirit. Neither was it a call to linger, but one to desist from my course and return to where I now belonged.

On such misunderstandings there may rest the fancy of many uncertain cravings, for we often choose what we seek without regard to wiser counsel, only to arrive weakened and humbled at the mercy of deliverance.

This was the course I was now on.

What followed had no precedent. I left the boundaries of reason and the third place to roam unrestrained in a world without harbour for my presence. Let it be clear: following my encounter with Douglas I was neither within the shelter of a third place or within the reaches of the physical world. I was lost to both and all but condemned to irrevocable isolation.

I returned to Freeland as one would follow a well-trodden path to sanctuary. Just as my father's spirit had guided him down from the fells to a place of comfort and familiarity, so too did I now crave a place of refuge. By following the trails of my mortal presence, etched into the elements and forms of a worldly landscape, I came to the consequence of my foolishness, for this was as much a pilgrimage of the mind as it was a journey of spirit.

It was here at Freeland that I was indeed to find refuge, albeit not the haven of peace and calm that I sought. My foolishness had brought me to an end where I was destined to remain forever, suspended in the ways of the past to torture generations of future souls. As comforting as it was to be amongst familiar surroundings and kindred spirits, there would come a time when mortal ties passed and memories faded to leave nothing but anguish at the isolation of my being.

That this did not come to pass was no achievement of self-will or good fortune. Neither was there a late reprieve by some benign authority to save a wayward son. There was no mystery, save the everlasting wonder of the act of sacrifice by one for another. It is through such selfless gifts of concern, such denial of self-worth, that small steps in the evolution of humankind are sealed.

The combination of my mother's spirit and her will to attend to – rather than dismiss – such sensitivities of insight as may be illuminated by the presence of a greater energy, was as crucial a moment as any in what I look back upon as a series of pivotal judgements and events in this strange journey. It was the complete harmony of body and spirit that acted in unity that day to reprieve one who was lost.

It was Freeland that saw the culmination of my turmoil. I had followed my elected ways to an end in which I had no choice. It was here that I arrived at the end of a treacherous path to confront the consequences of my actions, and it was here that salvation would, or would not, prevail.

Freeland was my sanctuary. As I came to the warm pulse of those familiar surroundings, I relaxed into a nostalgic view of memory; a timeless illusion that would be played and replayed as long as some faint marker of my life lay in the forms and ways of that place. What I perceived to be my mother was but a shadow of her physical self upon which I laid my own intractable illusions. I had no vision. I had no way of recognising any mortal form. In truth, the sight of my mother was no more than the whimsical turn of memory toying with a mind so bedevilled by fancy, so far from reason that sense had long since been lost to the giddiness of delusion. I relived the comfort of unconditional love with an eagerness that dispelled all consideration of reality.

I was between worlds and between poles of understanding. I dwelt in Freeland as one intruding upon the present. My view was conjured from the past by a mind that belonged nowhere. It is of no surprise to me that I should render such images that I perceived as real in all respects, whereas in truth they were no more than the last throws of my attachment to physical senses. I was still shedding my worldly connections and visualising my past from the narrows of the passage to eternal isolation. I had carried the grief of another beyond the limits of reason and was due to do so for the remainder of existence. This was to be the way of it for eternity; the continuous replay of worldly memories and passions; false comfort from loss and retreat from reason. I had come to an end without knowledge of it and without any liberty to change it. I was truly at the threshold of eternal isolation and all that travelled in its wake.

Then, by the grace of that monadic power, my fortunes turned.

No longer a party to my own fate, I was infused by the light of my mother's spirit. Through this, I was charged with the energy to release me from my incarceration and shown the way back to the spiritual world. In truth, I had no occasion to object, but the risk to my saviour was beyond my understanding and beyond the means of my spirit alone. It required both the unconscious will of my mother and her spirit's transgression of the spiritual code to invoke such power. To open a Third Way a spirit must leave a mortal body and soul. If this is not the result of death, death will be precipitated unless the spirit returns swiftly to support life – even then there becomes a weakness in life that remains as a scar upon the tissue that binds its elements together.

The passage once opened can only be closed by a departing spirit. Had I not left, the outcome would have forever darkened and silenced all life at Freeland.

Reason

O N   T H I S   O C C A S I O N,   I   left Freeland without companion or witness to my departure. I passed no threshold and trod no visible road. I did not so much step away as fade from it.

If my leaving might suggest a deliberate act of moving on to somewhere else of my choosing, then this was not so, for I had no knowledge of any destination, neither did I hold any expectation of arrival. I felt no desire or need to go, but neither could I resist the call to leave. I travelled by dint of expression, that was not mine, to transcend limits I no longer adhered to.

I rest when I am still, and wait for the light of understanding to know what is to come.

As I faded from the memories of one place, so I came to the uncertainties of another. There was no light, but there was a refreshing clarity as if a previously closed door had been set ajar to allow a new thought to seep through. This was different from before. I had been beckoned to enter and felt welcomed and at ease. The sense was one of benign company and merciful intent. I was amongst unseen, but not unnoticed, companions, and there was a presence, an air of calm and assurance that comes with the peace of reasonable cause. I no longer felt the oppressive closure of darkness; instead, I held open a long-empty place in my mind to receive the barest token of trust.

I rested in this newfound simplicity, absorbing as much as I could from my surroundings. The glow I felt was as a radiant reflection of my inner peace and a beacon of my readiness to grasp what was expected of me. In the very beginning there was a need to explore, to understand, and more – yes, to rebel against the proffered hand, to seize the moment to declare the right to know the first requirement made of man.

It was from here that I came to what I can only describe as uncertainty in my balance. It was not alarming, but much as I recall the sensation of giddiness from some sudden spinning of the body. A swirling sensation was bound with the appearance and disappearance of dusty reflections from earthly shades of dark and light as I was tossed in a misty kaleidoscope of spangled images and sepia landscapes. The revolutions were not violent but varied in pace and orientation. At first, I was passing through a wide trajectory with whispering mirages cavorting by, only to then spin away on some different orbit to witness bolder scenes with more familiar accents to them.

The change in texture and fume was both within and without so that as I twisted and spun in a variable haze of soft and hard vignettes, some familiar, some not, I recalled the feel and scent of each one. The collection appeared as a mixture of deeds and dreams, confused, forgotten, rejected, and perhaps buried beyond the reach of memory. In all that had been possible there were many occasions of choice, and the one I had chosen was presented to me to bear witness to the wonder of what I had once been.

And there was more. Not only did I live again through images and ways familiar to me, but also through hitherto unseen light and shapes of such varying texture and composition as to have no resemblance to any mortal or material form known to me. Whispers I knew as wise counsel were drowned in the discordance of unyielding contradiction, contesting for the right to lead my will on some other course as they pulsed through arcs of my gyration. Just as the turmoil of imagery before me would vary in passage and intensity so did the oscillation within me vibrate to alternate occasion and cadence. This was no appointment for interpretation, there was no necessity. The sounds were truths, the light clarity, and the composition the history of choice.

I was carried across pages of poetry that spun a trail of melodic metaphors so that all I once said and thought could be brought to account. This confusion of imagery and tone encapsulated my existence. As blood and bone once filled my body so now verse and spiritual awakening filled my being, coalescing as some star-like relationship to illuminate an unimpeachable spectacle of life as seen through the distant eye of some impassive high-throned judge.

There was no charge of blame or sense of retribution. This was not conducted as a trial of shame or even as a court of forgiveness to assuage a troubled conscience. It was the testimony of truth, as clear a statement of fact as could be given by any council for a life past. Just as I had been obliged to face my innermost thoughts and motives to account for my actions leading up to my death, so now I was being asked to look beyond recent memory to more dim and distant recollections of past deeds. It was the first step in shedding personal persuasions of truth.

This activity was revealing in many ways, but above all else it was to become clear that this was part of a more wholehearted cleansing process that comes to a point where life is placed in the arc of something much greater: a grain of sand within a dune, within a castle, within a desert, is neither one nor all together, that is until it falls; only then is something lost and something understood; only then is there a oneness of knowing.

The distinction between life and the greater realm of existence is meaningless in the physical world. They are separate: imperfect and perfect in nature. But in the duality of both, the two become one and exist in harmony in the fullness of reality.

Whether it is through the passage of life or thereafter, reality remains. In the physical world, it is the perception of things in their own right: the knowledge of their presence and an understanding of their use in the frame of the waking mind – the consciousness *to* being for its own sake. In the spiritual world, it is an understanding of reason: what is and what is not in the greater realm of all else that has gone before and is yet to come – the unconscious understanding *of* being.

In each case, reality is the conclusion of all possible

deliberations; as full a level of understanding and settlement of purpose as can be, given the condition in which it is known. To know the completeness of it all is as unattainable for one as it is for the other; it is a goal that requires the two expressions for being to be as one: a single entity without allegiance to coveted notions of dominion. It requires unity.

The intensity of this experience continued as though through my memories. Again and again the streaming images and distant callings cascaded through me as I was confronted with variable plays from diverse perspectives to tear down the facades of disguise and pretence. As each faded from me, so I was left with the intractable granite of the most basic motives of life. I had little doubt as to the outcome, as successive acts revealed the dulled hues of mistaken actions and discarded opportunities. This persistent, repetitive performance peeled away the masks I had acquired to leave me with a refreshed, clearer picture of my journey. There was no sense of judgement upon me; there was no admonishment or threat, just a clear projection of what I knew to be true. As I came to this conclusion, so my sense of balance returned and I came to rest in the simple state of stillness once more.

Whatever it was that remained within me as a gesture of lasting standing must now be expunged by this flight of all that I had once thought real. My mind was darkened by the absence of trustful memory; I was stilled by my inadequacy of undertaking as much as I was by a lack of any passing influence upon me. Perhaps, this was it. I could not distinguish the real from the imaginary or the end from the beginning. The nadir of my being had been reached.

*

Much as I welcomed such bouts of uncertain consciousness to break through the unrestrained periods of deep emptiness, they were as little compared to the joys of what was now slowly teasing me from my slumber. I came through strata of insensibility to a new height, wherein all clarity and richness of tone I could finally believe in the familiar feel of another's presence.

As a child banished for some misdemeanour to rest in a repentant bed awaiting pardon, I was ushered from my somnolence to find the warmth of forgiveness tearing away the folds of sleep. I listened to savour the hushed, but increasingly discernible, quiver of my name and fought to find those most familiar images in my mind to give substance to the stirrings I now felt. The closeness of something so missed, so dear, and yet so far from reach, was as consuming of all that I could give, as ever was a struggle at birth. I felt a deep, primeval urge to break free of capture and release myself of all promises, no matter the consequences, for just one moment with my yearning.

The now unmistakeable echoes of my name pulsated all around and through me like some soothing metronomic lullaby. I was suffocating in my frustration to reach out and grasp the source of comfort, to devour the sweet taste of that which was so precious to me. I was all but lost in the injustice of frustration and self-pity when it came to me, godlike in the enormity of its comfort. I was no longer alone.

I came to know the voice of my father as I would the words of my thoughts: a silent appeal from the unutterable universe. It was I who was not listening, and it was I who was not reaching out. There were now two instead of one and a conversation instead of a monologue.

A second silent voice was with me as sure as that of my own.

I thought, and as I did I felt the words pass from me to return afresh in kindly fashion to rest before passing into memory. This was as clear a peal of notes as that of my own whispered musings. I heard no sound but knew the words as surely as the secret callings of my mind.

I had an answer; it was all that I sought and could have asked for. From loss, confusion, and despair, there would now be guidance. Just as I had once known comfort that was unshakeable in its presence, so now I would know the surety of words passing from that same trusted source. I had been found by and, in turn, had come to my father.

From henceforth I felt the grace of hope smile upon me. I look back upon a moment of release. I had dwelt so long upon a call from within that I had become prisoner to my deliberations. This was yet another turn in the everlasting quest for understanding. A gaping chasm, an imponderable vacuum, a deep and silent pit that imprisons the mind had been exposed for what it was: a denial of the need to see beyond the study of mortal reason alone.

*

Such entreaties for knowledge, for answers, have lingered long in the breast of humankind, and at the very last there always remains a dreadful confusion between the quest and its cause.

To search for meaning and reason in a desert has no reward, for the view and the truth is the only view and the only truth.

The cause of reason becomes part of the quest: the hunted becomes the hunter, becomes the hunted. The final question is in danger of becoming the answer.

*

For now, though, a page had turned and once again I was presented with the wherewithal to continue my education. To know and understand the relationship of thought to deed and the consequence of change thereafter is but a small part of evolution. To consider what it was that first freed the mind to move to new pastures in life is to dwell upon the very nature and purpose of existence. To know this is to guide the wheel of evolution to the end of its journey.

The simplest act can sometimes be the most rewarding, and so it was with the presence of my father: intertwined with my thoughts, calling my name, responding to my ignorance, and anticipating my needs as though already spoken and laid bare for all to witness.

Truths

'You are and always will be the First: the Truth, the Story, and the Guardian of both.'

*

The words floated into reach as my father became a part of my landscape once more.

It was as if I heard from within. I was the newborn, the unspoken word, and the unconscious thought. I had always been there, still and timeless. I was there before life and I was there after death. Once more I was to become truth – the reason behind all things, the fire that drives the spirit that moves all else on its unquenchable journey.

I had never been anything other. I had returned from whence I had first come. My life as Christian had been no more than a step in an odyssey. My time in the physical world was as nothing, for I had been born many times. I had come from the womb of creation to balance forces and bring life into what, otherwise, would have remained without challenge, forever.

Truth is there, hidden and awaiting discovery; there are no new truths, only islands waiting to be named.

Truth is a worldless dimension of being, a dimension so artfully concealed that until it is revealed it is without words or meaning. Such hidden truths are the future. They are as much a part of being as darkness is a part of ignorance.

If I were to know these truths again, then it would be through the voice of my father as reader of such concealments. Father had become, to me, the sound of being. He had passed through to become spirit once more, and these wisps of fanciful imagery and light were as plain in their statement of my being as to allow me to believe in my existence as a continuation of truths – of knowing and, if not yet, of understanding.

For now, I was to remain as Christian in the spirit world – just as my father would remain as Father and guide – until all memories, all traces of my mortal life had passed. Only then would I be free to continue my journey.

*

'You are perpetual.'

*

The knowing of it came to me as if to transcend worldly doubt and argument. The spirit needs neither evidence nor persuasion. It seeks no assurance or confirmation of its being; it is united with all things, be they living or stilled.

It is lasting and not bound to the world of matter. Spirits exist as continuous energy. The same energy that laid the foundation for life remains as a companion thereafter. There is no life without spirit and no difference between one form of spirit and another, except for that which each spirit knows and briefly retains of a lifetime. On its return to the spiritual world, the spirit sheds memories and attachments to all things physical so that it may return pure in its understanding of existence.

*

'You are companion to the soul.'

*

The two are distinct but quintessential parts of life. Neither spirit nor soul can be compared to the physical form; neither has shape nor carries any likeness to the physical being they occupy. Both are attached for a lifetime to one and all forms of physical life. There is no physical life without spirit and soul – the three are inextricably linked in the ways of life. I was to think of a spirit as the conduit for all seen and unseen forces, a gateway to all influences on life. It is a filter that tests the wisdom of behaviour, a defence that protects against the subjugation of a greater will; it is the arbitrator of conflict and the bestower of conscience. It is a guardian of the soul and a protector of spiritual origins.

For a while, at least, I would seek to compare these truths with the notions of life that I still clung to, but gradually one would burnish the other to more fully expose the splendour of both.

I was to look upon spirit as a collection of knowledge of all things beyond the range of physical accomplishments. It is a benign companion in all conscionable matters arising from life. It is a blueprint for behaviour of the hidden mind that rests within all mortal beings and takes its place freely in all life without judgement and prejudice. As well as guiding from within, I knew that spirits could retain the ability to interact with each other – in many ways and senses – just as I did with my father, freely exchanging our thoughts through our energy and will. At times, though, in other places and circumstances, such benefit of collective wisdom shared in this way with the physical host is as prone to the amenability of the mortal being's will to receive and acknowledge such signals. This obliviousness to spiritual guidance can be both a barrier and control for the future of life. As I would come to learn, it is not the prerogative of spirit to impose its ways upon the order of things.

My father's words ebbed and flowed around me and I savoured the detail of each as it washed into place within some lost memory. It was a refreshing of faded truths that had been suppressed by less wise counsel, and I felt a certainty that comes with the cleansing of the inner vessel.

This was indeed both a time of cleansing and renewal. The spirit had been cast free from life and had parted from the soul. The severance from both was as wounding to the spirit's resolve as any loss known to mortal life.

The soul is life's record. It is a part of the greater book that charts events that come from, or have influence upon, life. All life has spirit, but it is only life kindled with the freedom of will that has both spirit and soul; for it is only through the course of wilful, conscious action that the natural passage of events can be influenced and, at the very end, accounted for by the soul.

In contrast to this flow of understanding, when these considerable and yet plain truths rested so comfortably within me, there were periods of silence when I dwelt on my thoughts to make what I would of that which had been given. At times, a sharpness of mind focused the clarity of my father's guidance even more, so that I was left with an indelible image of spirit as a rightful keeper of long-buried principles of reasonable cause. On other occasions, I sensed that I still carried unfulfilled longings, for as my father had said there would be, there were moments of dull shades of thought when I would drift between beckoning shores, unable to reach one for the pull of the other.

At times it appeared inevitable that, if left to my deliberations on such tides of fluctuating courage and caution, I should be drawn to wander in the middle ways between certainty and doubt. It seemed there was a struggle between the lure of life and the appeal of what was to come after. The legacy of one was competing with the promise of the other, and I had not yet grasped the sense or purpose of either.

As I came to this uneasy settlement of mind, and as though in response to my unspoken need, my father's presence once again filled my thoughts.

*

'Some spirits falter in their journey.'

*

My return to a spirit form was through an ephemeral way, a third way that opened in response to my leaving the mortal body. This is the only way to move between the two worlds. It is open but briefly to allow a spirit to pass from one life and one world to another. It was given to me, however, to forsake that opportunity. It was now that my father's tone became more laboured and hushed.

My return to Freeland was as one without energy or nurture. I was without means of survival or release from mortal grasp. I owed my presence there and my eventual freedom to the intervention of another's guardian spirit, one that had shared my ways in life and had been prepared to sacrifice their time for mine. Without this offering, I would surely have been on a different course to the one I now travelled.

There was a silence between us, during which I was invited to reflect on the alternative to this moment. I can only say that I was uneasy as to the consequences of what had been without volition on my part and yet now seemed to be of such significance to my future.

I had exposed others to danger by my actions and now it was I who was being held to account. I had been given the benefit of an unbiased view of events to show how I had come to the now of my being. For all that had been and all that was to come after, it took but one false step to dislodge my being from memory and the pages of life. I had had my first lesson and learnt how close the presence of each is to their last – in both worlds.

*

'You, I, and all spirits are as one body mixed.'

*

We came from the same seed and shared the same fruits of life and we return to the kernel of existence to begin again the cycle of growth. I was not to see my father as I once had done. Instead, I was to know him as one with whom I shared the gift of life. Where we had once lived as two bodies, we were now as one, an unconscious recognition of the fullness of everything. There was no difference between us. By sharing knowledge from the vast arena of creation, we would come to the same end.

My father knew my thoughts as I knew his, and I was no longer alone. My senses were no longer cloistered by the self-full insight of mortal life. Instead, I was to roam in the freedom of account and understanding until I was committed to fulfil the charge placed upon all our kind.

Until this moment, I had not dwelt upon the manner of my finding or on the part I was to play. I was as a drop of water falling into an ocean, only to continue seeking knowledge of myself despite having become something much greater. I was no longer alone, no longer an expression of one, isolated from all others. I had become that which held and nurtured what I had once been. I had been blind to what was around me because I was seeking my future through my past; my vision was as one part instead of the whole that my father had begun to open before me.

It was not a competition between what I had been and what I had become that I was to resolve, but in my father's words, it was an alliance of necessity that I was to discharge.

Everything that is said or done has a part to play in the final act. It is not for one deed or single action to be denied as having no bearing upon what follows. Each has its place in the particle mosaic that binds one to next and the first to last. Being is eternally tied to ways that may seem without relation to the present. We are nothing if not of the past, and yet because of unknown myriad associations within and across boundaries we know nothing of it. The past is a mysterious part of the present and there is no escape from it. It is written in character just as it is written in the folds of nature. The past accompanies each moment and every player in a spiral that sets course against course until time stops for some poor soul. The way is lost and what had seemed a clear and reasonable route to ply has led – through no discernible fault or identifiable cause – to an end: not yet The End, but nevertheless an end as unexpected as it may have seemed unaccountable.

My course, as all others before me, was just as described, up to the point where my return to Freeland from a Third Way set me apart from the world where such endings are known only as a release from one's part in the next event.

The whole episode in Freeland had set the first step in what was to become the most extraordinary journey between two worlds. It was a new start for me, a path without partner or precedent, a turn without name, a maze without escape. The course set was not encumbered by authority and would lead me to part from those ties to ritual, order, and history.

As I absorbed the essence of my father, I could not help but dwell on the contrast between what I once knew as being as full a representation of everything as there ever could be, and now when I was to believe that I had not known but half of it. Yet, when confronted with this enrichment to life, I was still to rely upon my mind to expose its glory.

It was that last pale reflection of my past which still competed for my affections as I found myself floating away to an open and beautiful place in contrast to the unfamiliar enclosure I now found myself in.

*

'Mortal mind can only rest within the spiritual heritage of existence.'

*

I had drifted and my father knew it. My memories were of the mind that created them. Such gifts as I was experiencing with my father were the manifestation of knowledge, the first line of the first chapter of my continuing education.

The spirit is energy; energy that is harnessed by the spiritual core to feed a collective form of being, that in turn, governs existence. Spirits have had this power since the dawn of creation. Without this centrality of purpose, energy would be an unruly and disruptive force. Just as mortal beings could not exist without a heart to feed the mind that speaks of life, so we could not exist without this spiritual centre – not to know life, for we are not bound by mortal limits, but to know the place of life and to guide it through eternity to the end of its day. Mortal beings live to survive; spirits exist so life can survive. Without spirit there would be no life, and without energy there would be no spirit.

I had no wish to break the flow from my father; it poured through my being, invading, drowning, washing my worldly water clock clean.

*

'Yes.' My father had answered a question I had not asked.

*

My father had anticipated a question before I had framed it, bringing it to the fore of my mind to help me through the transition from one world to another. The images I had clung to were acquired as a result of all spirits' obligation to attend to mortality. My memory was the product of my mortal body's inner-self – my character. It was this portrayal of the self that I had brought with me and which I so fondly recalled.

I was still saddened by the nature of my departure, sadness now mixed with feelings for the father I once knew. My worldly father and my spiritual father were still as two to me, and yet one survived and knew me better than I had ever done or possibly ever would.

This newfound intensity of perception and emotion was as a whirlwind scattering my longings and desires across whatever it was that I now had come to rest within. I most certainly was not prepared for the sudden unwrapping of my inner self and my thoughts. My thoughts were both an outer layer to be shared in exchange for knowledge and a bed upon which to lay my spiritual musings. I was comfortable with that, just, but to lay bare my feelings, to completely expose that part of me for all to know was as shocking to my understanding as anything so far revealed.

It seems I had no refuge, no outward character in which to hide; my father was denying that part of me I knew as Christian and which I still believed to be at the centre of my ways. If not that, then what reflection of my being was I to carry? Where in all eternity's name was I? If not of body or mortal chains, of mind not free and thought not hidden, if not known or admitted, not denied or turned away, then what image would hold me still? I am of spirit and with spirit. My father is dead. I am with my father, so I am dead and yet I hear him as he hears me. All this I can accept, indeed more than that, I can believe, so it is not *what* or *where* I must ask, but *how*. How do I exist?

As the question came to me, so did it leave in search of that unachievable stillness that beckons the curious to their discovery. It was a plea that sought the comfort of wiser counsel; a cry that echoed across the ages; a prayer that waited for an answer: the truth that requires no further question.

The Beginning

M<small>Y FATHER BEGAN AS</small> all good fathers do.

*

'At the very start, at the very beginning of it all, there was one, and one order only.'

*

It was the order of certainty that governed all things without challenge, for it was tempered by unspoken reason and moderated by unquestioned belief. There was no limit to its rule, no goal or ambition, no debate or counsel to consider, and no court or judgement to pass. This was simply the way of it. It was a place of one accord without dissent or argument; a place of one moment without memory; a place with one meaning. It was the way before creation and life, the way before all things that accompany the uncertainties that come with division.

He had taken me back to before time began, and I heard as one would experience a dream – without knowledge of whence it came or the wherewithal to intrude upon its presence. All I could feel was the sureness of its message as it flowed through and around me as the story that began all stories.

*

The First Way was what we may now think of as the rudimentary particles of matter, but there was no coming together and no substance. There was the essence of spirit – the spark of life – but there was no life; all the building blocks, but no buildings and no builders. It was a place of plenty and paucity, of hope without opportunity, promise without expectation, and potential without fulfilment. All that was and would be within this place was countered and tempered by opposing and balancing forces so that equilibrium was maintained between the spiritual and non-spiritual presence. For every force, there was a counter, and for every particle an opposite. There was no life as we know it, just elemental and spiritual geometry, balance and certainty.

*

'It was the certainty of one which rested in the security of its being without impairment of its reason through question.'

*

It was enough to be, to exist – to have worth in a single reality without seeking something more. The value of existence was in its presence and nothing else. All that could be was dependent upon being and not upon the thought or introspection of it. This was both the barest and richest store of unbridled hope and fruitless promise ever assembled. It was all there had ever been, an unheralded, unspoken, universal singularity of everything.

In the reality of this union, this everlasting symmetry, there lay a languid co-existence between natural and unnatural forces adhering to physical and non-physical laws in a mutual – but inert, respectful paralysis. Fundamental to the stability of all that occurred in this harmonious but torpid cosmos of all things was the capacity of eternity to respond to the one constant that has no counterweight: Change. What takes place in the name of change cannot be undone, and slow as it may have been, as evolution casually sought to unravel the order of ages, so did the spiritual architects of this place seek to accommodate the consequences and counter the effects that arose, as if from the slow unfurling of a butterfly's wing, to effect a new tomorrow. It was change that stretched and tested the boundaries of this cosmos until, finally, a single event toppled the fragile durability of a unified existence. That event was to bring about the end of the First Way and replace it with the duality of physical and spiritual being. It was change that was to bequeath two distinct, but forever entwined, new worlds.

What that event was will never be known, for it was as much a part of the consequences as spirits once were. Whether it was charmed by cherubs or conjured by chemists, it broke the order of eternity to free the wiles of ages to install a new, less-disciplined regime to spin the wheel of evolution to new limits of forgiveness. It was the energy from this cataclysmic separation of the tangible from the intangible which triggered the dispersion of matter through the hitherto unchallenged parameters of order and stability to create the two worlds between which we now move so easily. Short-lived passageways were formed as particles of matter and metaphysical plasma were liberated from isolation to be hurled in rebellious juxtaposition and reactive reversal to eternal seclusion, coalescing at random into material and non-material forms in the newborn physical world. At first, matter and spiritual essence poured freely from one world to the next; but, as the material particles aggregated into more complex and massive forms, the balance between matter and spirit was broken. The remnants of the now uniting spirits in the old world coagulated into white energy to fill the voids left by the dispersed matter, until, all else having been separated from spiritual forms, the passageways closed forever to matter of any kind. What metaphysical plasma that remained locked in the new world became one of the constituents of early life, thereby retaining a link between the physical and non-physical worlds. But the balance that once existed was broken, and it was the physical form that now dominated.

As for us, my father had said, we were to become as

shadows – reflections cast adrift by some tomfoolery of change to mirror forever all that was lost from the First Way. We are hallucinations of the past, the bond of ages born from a marriage of spirit and dust to settle in a foreign place, full of contrast and contradiction to our origin. Light and dark, soft and hard, cold and hot, all are alien to spirit, as are the conflicting energies that fight for supremacy to rule in a place still fleeing from the parity of unity and harmony.

We utter the word to the inner voice, declare the note to the composer, the hue to the artist; above all, we are the conscience that forever carries the weight of change.

We pass unnoticed, as the gentle breeze that in a dream may drift across the sleeping eye to suggest the coming of dawn. We are as a shadow in the night, watching to ward off the fears of a restless mind. If we could be seen, it would be by one who sees the turn of fate set against the wheel of fortune, or he who tallies the count of injustice against the score of reason. We are not of substance or form. It is not for us to see or touch in the way we once alighted upon some small imperfection of order. We are far removed from that memory, and as bewitching as those treasures now seem, they are as little compared to the paradise of powers we have to see and feel beyond the outer skin and to hear and know beyond the given word. To call upon another's honesty of thought and to address their truest feelings without a moment's assertion to the gospel conveyed, is the most precious of gifts ever bestowed upon spirits. To know the single truth, to sense the solitary emotion, takes away all doubt. It dispels barriers of fear and uncertainty, it removes obstacles to generosity and goodwill, and even more, it defeats that plague of all communions since the demise of the First Way – that of disbelief and mistrust.

Mistrust was unknown in the First Way. There was no competition and no need to survive to the detriment of another. All spirits had but one goal and that was to maintain the equilibrium of existence. The seed of doubt was sown in the new world where spirits no longer controlled the delicate balance of response to change. In the absence of a governing force, all that remained in the vacuum was elemental chemistry to transform malleable constituents into inhospitable liquefactions and inanimate matter, from which evolution spawned self-governing entities without soul or spirit to moderate desire or behaviour. The result was the origin of life. Born into chaos, the response was to compete for the right to survive in a bleak and forsaken environment – no matter at what cost. In the circumstances, there was little choice, but the mould was made, and nature evolved from a set of intrinsic values to one that placed survival above all else.

*

This turmoil described by my father was witnessed by those undergoing metaphysical transformation in the First Way, and has remained as told in the core of spirit itself. However, the workings of the passageways and their part in this was not apparent to those left behind. It was presumed, by those remaining, that those spirits who had been lost when the ways were closed had been lost forever. In fact, the most remarkable outcome of this whole calamitous event was still unfurling in the new world.

The energy released during the separation of matter and spirit had partly been absorbed by spirits. It was this metamorphosis that enabled spirits to coexist and evolve with diverse material elements into forms of spiritually infused matter plasma. This proved to be the crucial point in the evolution of conscionable life forms. The spirits trapped in the new world, and now far removed from its controlling origins, used this elemental infusion to evolve into the fundamental metaphysical particle of life. In due course, spirits had transformed sufficiently to inhabit an elemental jacket to create the spark for life. It was now just a question of evolutionary gestation before emerging, as it were, from an egg into new strange forms of being. A spiritual compromise of necessity had brought a lifeline of conscionable energy to the new world. The birth of spiritual providence had been secured.

From life, it was but a short journey to death and the release of a spirit back to its ancestral roots. However, to reunite the two worlds had been an epic force of reactive behaviour and spiritual tenacity. The sacrifices made in the name of survival were not solely metaphysical innocence; spirit not only lost its identity, it also lost its known course. It had to relinquish its guiding principles to transform its ancestral rule from one of benevolent control to a new compassionate, guiding sovereignty. No longer was a spirit to be the sole arbitrator of the arrangement of things. The introduction of conditions ultimately conducive to physical life was to intrude forever upon the dominant order to impose an uncertainty of freedom and self-will upon this new world. On awakening, the spiritual energy had morphed into a junior partnership, an embryonic relationship with organic molecules to create a series of minor life forms. It was far removed from the old order of things and without doubt, in those early incarnations, a short-lived experience. Imagine if you will the earliest cellular life forms, constantly coupling, dividing and mutating into unstructured microscopic organisms with one thing in common: wilful energy. The will to survive as a physical entity had been augmented by spiritual reason. Slowly, there came a purpose to life and a means by which spirit would be able to continue its part in the timeless endurance of existence.

*

'We are now, I hope, close to answering your question, but there is one last part to reveal before I layout the completed montage.'

*

My father had brought me back to the crux of my question: How do I exist? I had come from a world without life to one with, through an occasion of change that had set in motion a journey of unchecked freedoms and longings. I had become an expression of existence through the nature of being for a purpose as yet untold. What was to follow would be a testimony to the everlasting nature of spirit and its part in this journey.

The return to the spiritual world, my father had told me, was no more than a reversal of the separation process, and varies little from what has occurred ever since, except in the originality of its occurrence. The release of the spirit from its physical form precedes death of the mortal body and focuses all its energy back into the spiritual core. The sudden contraction and expansion of energy as the spirit leaves the physical being creates what we now know as a Third Way to deliver the spirit back to the non-physical world. This is unremarkable, but those spirits first returning to the spiritual world were to find a strikingly different place to the one they had left. Instead of the turmoil of raw, elemental evolution that consigned them to the new world, there now appeared to be total annihilation: complete and utter emptiness, a vacuum, a plague-torn place bereft of all meaning. They had returned to nothing. Life had replaced the harmony of the First Way and now life itself was shown to be the end. The contraction and dematerialisation had been catastrophic enough to extinguish spirit in its wake. Imagine the distress. Imagine the consequences. One world, just born, so full of promise, and another dead and bereft of hope; the union of two, conjured by the breakdown of symmetry and order, had been thwarted by the vengeful ferocity of the fleeing hordes. Those now staring into the abyss would have seen only the reflection of their predicament: a few impoverished survivors without reason to be.

What horror indeed, had it been entirely so. In truth, it

appeared just as my father described. But those returning had travelled far across the boundaries of change; they had regressed to a place deep-set in their psyche – a very different place, both from their leaving and from the reality of their experience in the new world. Remember, they were the first to make this journey and, like me, they had yet to shed one reality for another.

They had, in fact, returned to the First Way at the very point they had left, and it was indeed barren as told. But the reality of their existence in the world they had just come from was one in which change is allowed to continue unchecked. Change without counter-change, without symmetry, and without balance requires a different order: it requires time.

Time had become the new order that placed events in sequence to relate them one to the other. They had come from a world of progression through time and occasions of change to one unaccustomed to either. If time could ever have existed in the First Way, it would have stood still, for the order they had once known never changed – or rather, it never changed without a sterilising counter-change. The First Way they had left had catastrophically dismembered itself, and now they had returned to a much altered place, one which had been frozen in its own brief history by the crystallisation of the remaining spirits after all matter had left. The cryogenic spiritual suspension of those who had never left the First Way was what now confronted those returning. They were not to know this as it occurred after their departure, but those who had sacrificed their freedom had done so on the very teeth of the closing jaws of annihilation. They may have done so in heroic desperation or intrinsic genius, but it was by any consideration unlikely to have been as a result of prolonged deliberation. For without matter the role of the spirit would have been without purpose, and so the course they took was the only choice: a suspension of all in the name of some greater undefined good. In the history of all things it would prove to be an act of heroic genius.

Those now resting on the edge of the abyss had, unknowingly, played their part in the greater good. They had brought back with them the key to unlocking that silent, desperate situation. Their very existence, their presence, their source of energy was to awaken the sleeping from their slumber. The same energy that flows between spirits as thoughts are exchanged, radiated out into the vacuum, searching for signs of existence. Just as spirits communicate by reading the spiritual mind and the energy trails left by life, so they scanned the stillness about them. It was this intrusion, slowly seeping into the bleakness, that exposed the true mode of their hitherto hidden world. It was they who initiated the annealing process to release the entombed from their cocoons. The spiritual world had been reborn out of the remnants of the First Way by the release of the Immaculate Eternal Spirit. Those returning had been the first to traverse between two new worlds to forge an enduring union between physical beings and spirits, and between life and existence. A new age had begun.

*

At this point, my father had paused, as if to affirm the enormity of this supreme occasion in the birth of life. What had begun as a story had become a passage of account for all reason and purpose. What had been told had flowed by means of its veracity to the point where words had become intruders in a portrait of beauty that shone with its own light to illuminate the subject.

*

'All this I know as surely as I know that I am Spirit.'

*

His words were as my own, coming from somewhere deep within the core of my being.

I knew the past as the fullness of what it was, and not as the worn words of some ancient lore hastily re-penned by the inventive mind to bolster a fading memory. Spirits have no need of memory. We are all able to replay the past and relive such moments at will to guide our judgement. This is why we can so readily read each other's thoughts, for we spirits are so very much alike. It is only the lingering influence of our mortal experiences that briefly separates us from our ancestral gifts.

Life has seen many a new dawn and fading twilight since that first glow of rebellious freedom. But as long as the spirit remains a part of it, life will have only one beginning and one end. This *was* the beginning. The spark that ignited the fire to create the material universe also lit the slow-burning fuse of mortality. Before this moment there was nothing – that still, silent, torpid inertia of perfect harmony that may be known as 'nothing' waited patiently for a weakness, that one moment of disorder that was to begin the charge to obliteration and the end.

Yes, this was the beginning of life, but it was also the beginning of the end to life. For in this new world the order had changed, and the course of life now held existence in its palm – in contrast to the First Way where it was existence alone that ruled. The tie between spirit and matter had been shattered, and there could be no return to such a singularity of existence again.

Ever since the moment of creation when chaos entered the new world, the spirit has been seeking to counter the effects of change. To say this is a never-ending task is to mislead, for if change – and therefore the predisposition to chaos – could be ended, then life itself would end and there would be a return to the old inert order found in the First Way. The new world would have become as the old, and the two would exist as silent twins, impotent and unvarying. The Age of Nothing would truly have come, for if spirit were to fail in its task to restore order, life would be destined to come to an end of its own accord as the physical world, with all its contradictions and imperfections, hurtled into the abyss that would be the end of reason. In this case, the spiritual world alone would remain in the name of existence. But, as such an existence would be bereft of any form of matter and as without matter to control, spirit has no reason to exist, so that too would become an end. In both scenarios, so bleakly described, life comes to its conclusion and with it condemns the spirit and the very essence of existence to poverty.

However, if a spirit is able to regulate the change brought about by life, it is conceivable that life might survive to ensure the continuation of existence for the next, and possibly greater, fulfilment of being through some new form of consciousness that knowingly accepts unconscious rule, thereby creating an alignment of two worlds for the betterment of one, more harmonious, way. Life would succeed matter as nature's clay, unconsciously bending to spiritual laws instead of undoing its work.

Since that first small break of order, change upon change has compounded disorder into chaos and impending catastrophe. The headlong rush to freedom has morphed into a manic propensity to seek self-induced annihilation. The rate of change multiplies as some plague would feed upon the weak to sate its appetite for supremacy, and through all this, the circle of physical life ebbs and flows and comes again to break upon the rock of Creation's reason to find the passage bared. 'No ... go back from whence you came,' comes the cry of ages. 'What light has lit your way?'

Without that light of understanding, life cannot break free of the mould in which it is cast. Without shedding the notion of perpetual self-governance, life will not realise the necessity of the coming together of physical and spiritual reasoning to the fulfilment of both.

Such a proposition is so far in advance of the present state of the conscious mind, that it is a view beyond reach.

For all that has passed and all that is to come, there has been and will continue to be an inevitability of misguided intent that will conspire against the rule of order to deliver everlasting equilibrium.

*

This account of the birth of the new world was used by my father as the start of an unfolding montage of the reason for life, one that contributed much to my education and belief in what I was bound to do. As he relayed it to me, this was undoubtedly the origin of the physical world and the conception of a new era for spirits. But it was more; for me it was a start, the beginning of a journey of understanding that would transcend boundaries of belief and the isolation of a single horizon to life.

I had asked a question and been shown so much more than the answer. I felt humbled and excited to have been given so much so freely. In all that my father had spoken of, woven so intricately and so delicately in the fabric of truth as to appear inseparable from it, came a gift of affirmation that transcended the teaching and stayed me with a certainty of the way of it. This was more than mere knowledge, this was an infusion of belief into the very essence of being.

I know that I did not sleep, I had no need, but I was free to dream, and following our release from the enormity of creation there was a tacit acknowledgement between us that I should reflect on the full weight of all that had been said before moving on with my education.

I had my answer with such a fullness of sensation that all I was required to do was to listen as the symphony of sounds swirled about me. I existed as a consequence of necessity. It was as my father had said: spirits countered change, but they did more, they had a divine role within creation to extend life beyond the frailties of the physical form. To journey through ages to renew and enable matter to transcend the boundaries of physical possibilities, was evidence enough that spirit was the conductor to the composer's masterpiece. It was this composition of effort, this collaboration of distinct forces reaching for a greater achievement through the endeavour of two in favour of the labour of one, which had reawakened a sense of purpose within me. I had had a lesson and been invited to absorb the message of renewal, as much for my own regeneration as a fact of indelible potency. I had been given an infusion of new reason, and for the first time had begun to see the significance of something from within, instead of vesting belief in the vague illusions of reality from without. My insistence on equating substance with images, and not the body truth, was as flawed as any mirage in a desert of shifting horizon and faint heart. The irony was that I understood more without physical senses than I had ever done with. The extent of my ignorance in clinging to my former self-delusion was slowly dawning upon me as an unwelcome inheritance from the process of creation itself. Perhaps, it was as an inevitable consequence of division, or perhaps it was as the result of some later turn in evolution as physical beings sought to dominate the world they saw as theirs alone.

Whatever the origin of this dark emptiness of purpose, I felt I had touched the light.

The Gift

IT WAS AS THOUGH I had been carried to an exit; an escape from the haze of an uncertain mind that had been drawn between two shores of attraction until my capacity to choose had been shorn of all reasonable judgement or notion of right or wrong. I had drifted between the hard conscience of memory and the dreamlike spectre of the future on a tide that had no place in the world I now belonged to. As I turned from one horizon to the other, I would find that what had once been real had become an illusion and what had been a dream would become all too real.

In all of this, the 'I', the centre of my being, had yet to find rest. I still viewed my existence from the living world. I clung to the past as an anchor of stability and viewed all around me from its hold. It was my mind – my 'I' – that had yet to accept the new reality of being and bridge the divide between two worlds, the divide between the reality of life and the fullness of existence, the divide between being as one alone and being as all things together as one.

*

The quiet hollows of the mind reverberated to a sullen silence: deaf, without need to hear; dumb, without occasion to ask; blind, without dreams to see: words fell into spaces between clean pages, littering derelict schools; wisdom, stiff, apologetic, a graceless statue without rhyme; lost, vacant and wanting, waiting for reasonable cause. There was no other, no substitute, no choice or possible need to consider.

*

When matter broke through the ties of order, spirit was cast to bond with the physical world to spark the seeds of life. As time and evolution tussled with the chaos of creation, so spirit fused with life's offspring to embody its ways. The physical mind became the host for the spiritual 'I' of endeavour to guide its wayward child through the next step – the next incarnation of matter. From a docile parody of soulless virtue and a seemingly endless order of certainty that bore no threat to perpetual impotence, matter evolved into the wilful counterweight to spiritual piety, and a new, more rebellious volume of account was to be added to eternity's library.

When did this new beginning first reach out for answers? At some point in this evolutionary cycle, it seemed that life had assumed a countenance of superiority to its surroundings. From there, as my father had said, it was a small step to competition between new forms of life for the right to dominate and survive. If I had understood my father correctly, life had come to a mind of its own. It was in conflict with itself and, through spirit, with its origin. It seemed as though I, part seen, part seer, and part sought, now represented that dilemma. It was not a point of choice that I had been led to, but a dawning that I alone was insufficient to explain my reflection.

As I searched for a sign of what lay ahead, I mused on the part I was to play and its meaning. I was being encouraged to extend my grasp of all matters hitherto beyond the realm of mortal comprehension. The subtleties of my father's speech exposed a fuller vista of meaning to the creation he described. His expressive entreaties, I felt sure, were for me to embrace before coming to a certainty of my own accord to accept his call.

As one thought made way for the next, my mind, like a pendulum, swung between one cause and another, each as persuasive as the last and yet unable to hold me for longer than it took to release my grip on what the past had made me.

Once again, it was my father's guidance that broke through my wavering.

*

'The dichotomy you feel is both a legacy and a bequest.'

*

It is only through mindful certainty that reason can be exposed as being the forerunner for reality; it is only in the name of one reality, that existence can be understood. It is only through the mind that change takes its part in the slow-turning wheel of evolution, and it is only in the mind that spirit can conceive of the next counter to it.

I was being asked to reflect fully on the division of the mind as a consequence of creation, and to consider carefully the origin of its imperfection. The divided self I had framed as responsible for my distress had become eternal – a bedfellow of change, arising from the First Way and coupling with the spiritual 'I's' resolve to restore harmony to the new order. Without the presence of spirit to bind those first elemental particles of matter into the earliest life forms, it can only be assumed that the two worlds would never have evolved to their present realities, and the behaviour of both places would be bereft of a common centre of conscience.

It was this one consciousness, my father reminded me, this knowledge of the mindful self and the reason for it that I had to be sure of before I could go further. I had yet to know what it was that was required of me, but as I grew so would I become more attuned and my role would become clearer. My growth was not as age by time or physique by nature, nor was it to be by dominion over life. It was as a completeness of knowing the fulness of existence and the place of life within it. It is only by this that a spirit can apply purpose and reason to its role and thereby lend itself to the nurture of life. All spirits are the same. All have the same capacity, but not all have the same embodiment so not all are free to travel through the full spectrum of spiritual powers whilst residing in the physical form. Some roles are more taxing than others, but that cannot be foreseen. Only I would know when and to what undertaking such a calling would take me.

*

It was as if a horizon had been disclosed to relieve the monotony of a spinning carousel – a future sketched to entice a riddled head away from the merriment of blurred impressions.

If to see is to know and to know is to believe, then seeing is not a sense we spirits call upon to casually gaze at shapes and forms to wonder their worth or gauge their meaning. My father had, once again, inserted his thoughts into my own.

*

Seeing, as I once knew it, is no more than a picture to which the physical mind has applied some abstract name and notion of value to affirm the existence of what has been observed. But to a spirit, seeing is far more than a reflection. It is the knowledge of the scene within the greater compass of existence. It is the absorption of all thought and motive, the capture of simple truths and the embodiment of complex callings. In our world, spirit is whole, but in the physical world a spirit has been bound within many different forms of matter since creation. Some spirits are released and return again and again, whilst others remain within the surrounds of matter for much longer. Some have never 'seen', never returned to the wider frame of reason; they still await the outcome of nature's exertions to free them from their tomb.

I had now become so accustomed to my surroundings that they no longer occupied my attention in any way. I was not inhibited by them, but if I were about to experience something more, then it would not only expand my conception of what was possible, but would establish a behavioural quandary. If I were to somehow see my father – or the presence of his spirit – would I need to know him as well? Indeed, would my father be the same father of my memories? If not, which of the two was to be my real father? Then again, if I were not to experience some picture of him, how was I to be sure that he was not me – that I was not delirious?

I had fallen again, so quickly, so easily, into the arms of my own fallible reasoning. I sought to regain my conviction and felt ashamed for so readily reverting to the cheerless comfort of scepticism. I waited, still and expectant, searching in my mind for images in the dark, like some burglar at midnight. And then, slowly, it came to me: there would be nothing to appreciate unless I opened … opened what? Did I need to know by believing, by disbelieving, by sensing, by separation from senses? By what? It would be up to me, just as it was up to me to let my father's voice into my thoughts, thereby stretching the boundaries of my mind to let him connect through me in some way. It was not sufficient in this world to be passive or to retain physical infatuations, there was a need to proactively generate … generate a shell! A skin!

An outer layer! Something that others, other spirits could detect, in the same way that those first returning spirits could radiate their energy into the still vacuum and detect the presence of those entombed spirits that had never left the First Way. I needed to release something from within that could see and be seen. I needed help!

*

'Which, if I am not mistaken, is where we left the lore of creation lying on the brink of discovery so very long ago.'

*

It is true that, like me, those first returning spirits sought a reflection of themselves. But they were not as they had once been. At first, they too were confronted with a dark emptiness. They had returned without the control they once had, and it was this fortuitous loss of spiritual authority that enabled them to free those trapped in their crystallised cocoons. Spiritual energy in its purest form is unadulterated by contagion with physical matter. However, as my father had already described, those returning had fused with elemental matter in their time in the new world, and it was the slow, warming release of these impurities that freed those left behind – those seemingly bound forever in the stillness of the past. Unlike all spirits since, those returning had not the wherewithal to shed their worldly attachments before entering their former world, for at this point there was no spirit world as we now know it. All those early spirits had found was bleakness, an emptiness of reason, purpose and hope.

It was only after the release of the Immaculate Eternal Spirit from the remnants of the First Way, that the counterbalance to the physical world was born. Until that moment, those returning spirits, embodied in matter as they were, had lost their identity; they had lost their spiritual ethos.

My father's words found me as I became as those very spirits once were.

*

'Spirit *is*, because it exists, and thereby it fulfils the potential *of* being and the reason *for* existence.'

*

From those few words began the mastery of reason. That ethos, that spiritual genus, had been sullied by matter as it spiralled from order through unnavigable darkness into the raging fires of chaos before bedding with nature. Life has no single identity to which it must conform. The first animated forms lived and died without reason – other than to live again through their own energies. In time, as more dominant creatures emerged and conscious reason evolved, the ethos for life became as evidence sufficient enough for existence. '*I am*,' it reasoned, 'therefore I exist.' The 'I' of the self-full creature had spoken. Mortal life, it supposed, had reason enough *to* its being without need of higher authority or the necessity to consider its part beyond that which it could see.

So it was that those first returning spirits had lost their purity. They had lost their way and their place in the hierarchy of belief. Form had usurped place as the essence of being, it had become as master to its maker. The role of spirit in the First Way, had changed in the physical world, and those now returning had first to shed the ethos inherited from their time with life. Matter – that had engineered change in the physical world, could not be allowed the same freedom in the new spiritual world. The intrusion of uncontrolled trajectories of phosphorescent trails of combusting matter radiating into the very domain of orderly somnolence was anathema to those now roused by it.

My father had paused, as though to reflect on this momentous occasion and its significance to all that came thereafter. I refrained from interruption. I knew there was more to come. When he began again, it was with a much slower delivery.

*

'What is given changes all: the gift changes the giver, changes the receiver, changes the gift – which is no more.'

*

I seized the sense of what came to me: the balance between the giver and the receiver, the gift offered and the gift received, change. What passes for fortune for some may be as poor fare to others. So it was with the light of fire that freed and then confronted the awakened spirits. It revived energies of old, and stimulated the stilled sense of universal assembly and collective accountability for all who bring about disturbance to the equilibrium of eternity. But it also transgressed boundaries that had been redrawn after the demise of the First Way. That light of fire, in turn, now threatened order. Matter no longer had a place in the new spirit world. The release of one party had, therefore, to be countered by the binding of the other; those who returned energy to those who had lost it had to be bound from further exhibition. To maintain the spirit world as it was – uncontaminated by physical substance – those now with matter had to be made as those without, there was no choice; so much had transpired to deprive those returning with diminished powers that only those remaining still had the means to control matter.

Those returning were bound, not as I had thought with skin or shell, but with trust: a gift in kind for a gift given to free those returning from the grasp of matter. By releasing all matter to a fading trail of physical attachments, a spirit was to return to immortality in a timeless affirmation of its ways.

With the exception of those who had never left the First Way, all spirits have lost their purity. It is the sacrifice that has had to be made to account for that one act of change – now so distant – that was not countered. The result of all this is that ever since those first returning spirits, a spirit has been bound by this gift of trust to not release matter into the spiritual world. Mortal values are shed for indelible beliefs as a sign of trust before entering the spirit world. It is as much a part of spiritual being as skin or shell is to matter in the physical world.

*

I had been given all this, not to see, but to know the final truth: the truth without question. It was not as shape, or form, or impression of agreeable image, neither was I to cast aside all preconceptions as to what was possible; instead, I was to relate to all about me through the simplest principle of being: existence precedes essence. It is enough in itself, just to be – without question and without reason. The belief in existence before all else, regardless of the manner, purpose or nature, is the most fundamental rationale for being able to attest to life. Without such, there is no witness to behold, no testimony to truth, and no judgement to be made. To perceive, I had first to believe. There was no other way.

From the tone and delivery of these words and by my father's gesture, his offering of himself, his fellowship, I concluded that all I needed had been laid before me. I had been led to the gate and needed to make that final commitment of my own free will to pass through and to experience the truth of what I already knew to be true. Another way existed, a way without compromise but full of compassion, a way without illusion but full of illumination. I no longer had any doubt, and I relished the opportunity to move on with the full assurance and belief that what I sought was already within and waiting to be acknowledged.

One Being

THIS WAS A POINT in my journey that I look back on frequently; it was the point at which I first had the notion that physical perception and metaphysical truth might be insufficient to ever explain the part each played in its contribution to a greater understanding. They were as two halves of existence separated by chance to revolve around each other in a dance of seemingly fateful repulsion.

There was, without doubt, a physical world: all matter rebelling against order and array – it was but an inevitable outcome given the persistent exuberance of change. Equally, there was a spiritual world: a place of loss, regret, and resigned subservience to an errant sibling who cavorted in the sparkle of burning unity. If the two were ever again to become a meaningful whole, there had to be a fusion of understanding and wisdom to corral physical endeavour with spiritual purpose.

It was this proposition of the two coming together in harmony, instead of the ritualistic cycle of regeneration as in death or birth – like a switch – to begin again the pilgrimage to understanding, that brought me to the realisation that both physical and metaphysical representations coexisted – not as a conveyance for the other, as I had begun to believe, but as two halves of an answer that sought the same question: the union *was* the quest; the answer was known, it was a return to the past through the future. In which case it was the question that was sought, but such a question that neither spirit nor life alone could ask, for that would be to the exclusion of the other and thereby the wrong question.

At this stage, then, it was not a matter of choice or transition that I was required to make, but simply an irrevocable acknowledgement that this was the way of it. To understand one, I was to leave the other behind.

The question that remains, therefore, is how can spiritual and physical union be harnessed to the betterment of both? How is it to be indelibly impregnated into the psyche of being?

All that my father had told me, in a way so simple as to embed the veracity of it in my mind as a story that could be recalled whenever I had need to, had somehow coalesced to this point where I was ready to move forward.

*

As soon as I had come to this simple conclusion, I came to relish a new awareness – a sense of recognition from within. I had an insight into the motive for being. I felt an interweaving of emotional tone and body of thought – it was as though another sense had come upon me and unlocked some closed corridor to new depths of feeling. As surely as I had once rested at ease within the isolation of a solitary frame of mind, so did I now hold my father's presence as connecting with my own. We shared a commonality of existence as complete as if we were united within the same space and the same circle of life. Not only did I know his thoughts and communicate through them, but I was now as much a part of him as he was of me. I perceived the tenor of his being from within, instead of a mere glance from without, and it was so much more than the physical manifestation had ever portrayed. He was without physical attributes, and the characteristics that adorned my mind had been washed away. Yet, there was much to recognise and much more to learn as we romped like metaphysical will-o'-the-wisps on autumn's murky muse. The skittish joy that took hold of our behaviour is, as I was beginning to appreciate, a trait of spirits who appear to readily oscillate between profound matters of creation and the light-hearted, inconsequential chaff of chatter.

We were the same. There were no longer any distinguishing features between us. The restraint of hierarchy between father and son was gone; the customs of behaviour were relaxed and the formality of our relationship was replaced by newfound freedom to expand the potential of our collective energy. For the first time, I was conscious of my thoughts no longer being limited by confused fancies of wonder or doubt. They were statements of certainty and more, so much more. I felt my father's spiritual presence more keenly than ever, as though the fusion of our energies had brought about a recognition of each other in our own right. It was as if, on the one level, the two of us existed independently together, but on the other level we became confirmed, united in a union of mind and spirit. I was able to discern the knowledge of my father's mortal life through the very essence of his spiritual existence. It was as though I was dwelling within him as a reader of all the passion and sense and expression of life as he knew it.

Beneath our thoughts, I learnt, were layers of belief and trust upon which judgements and turns of nature rested. The unexplained, impulsive response to another's presence was revealed as a sharpness of spiritual sense. It was not of attraction or aversion for no apparent reason, but of endorsement, or rejection, of a creed for living that runs through the physical character to leave the thought and purpose of all things done. It seems that these personal traits are as clear to a spirit as any distinguishing bodily feature is to a mortal being. Only through the spiritual antennae acting as a guardian to physical life can such acute judgements be received to guide a receptive mind to a course that is not entirely one of free choice.

I knew the inviolability of spirit as if it had been laid before me, writ large in indelible ink on parchments of ageless permanence. I had forgotten the forfeiture of such fallible physical senses as sight, and I no longer mourned the departure of dull impressions of wonders that were once presented to me by these powers. In their place was no greater spectacle, but sharper and clearer recognition of the whole and the part played by each in its disclosure. That which I once knew as my father was still my father, but I knew him now through a shared purpose of being as well as by the old character of memory.

The two halves of one being had come together to give account of the whole self. It was as if a portrait had come to life within me to share the secrets of its colouring. From the first to last I knew the hand that stroked the canvas to brush life into the man.

My father had a grace of spirit and dignity of being that had been hidden from me by my infatuation with shape and form. The many gestures of his spirit had passed me by; I had failed to recognise, to give way to my own inner senses, and I had been the lesser for it.

I was enveloped in the intensity of the discovery as I perceived the heights and depths of my understanding of him. Such qualities as I may have only glimpsed before now, and assumed belonged to the realm of human life alone, were displayed as the bedrock upon which the spirit flourishes and upon which it lays the measure for all life. Whereas I once saw compassion as mortal due alone, I now knew the pain of injustice and the angst of desecration felt by his spirit for all things living or stilled. I saw the degree to which trust and care could extend to the placing of one stone upon another as in the building of a wall to shelter a flock, or to the comforting of an ailing neighbour, or to the pleasure of aiding the spring of birth in a newborn lamb. Where there had been love, I saw a protector of honour and a guardian of the weak and untutored. Where there was fury, it had been directed within at some modicum of self-weakness or short-sighted behaviour – but never without, that was the reserve of regret and soulful pity.

All of this was given to me to wonder at, but I was also invited to reflect: upon the sadness of unfulfilled dreams; upon the depths of despair encountered for loss of life of all kind; upon needless waste or senseless sacrifice, and upon the shedding of a tear that was not the prerogative of humankind alone, for I knew the sensation of weeping for lost causes. I had not known what weight could be borne by a turn in a path trodden, or what load could be so lightly released by the recovery of a broken wing. In life, my father's spirit had been hidden from me, not by design but by the shuttering of insight so lamentably absent from the mortal gift of seeing.

The mortal body is heir to many weaknesses and failures, but it also hosts marvels of sense and intellect that can inculcate a belief in its own infallibility. In the absence of any representation to the contrary, the mortal mind cannot conceive of any other possibility. It is this tireless allegiance to self-belief that is its greatest liability. Belief in any other comparable life-force is beyond the comprehension of self-constraining sensibilities; it is also beyond the gift of language and thereby deaf to the reasonability of argument. It is not until the images of mortality are set free to dwell with the potency of spiritual existence that a greater appreciation of the place of one to the other becomes possible. It is only at this stage, the meeting of mortal and immortal consciousness, that the fullness of reality becomes apparent.

I had known my father from both worlds, and through his spirit I had been given an insight into the powers that hitherto would have seemed the sum of witchcraft and quackery. A spirit can sense other spiritual presences about it, regardless of whether stilled – as in a trail left on inanimate matter by a passing traveller – or whole – as in the spiritual cohabitation of life. It can also replay past experiences and share those with other spirits when called upon. I had been told the tale of spiritual past and through this had come an understanding of old and new worlds, of parts played and lost, and of the birth of life. It was a story that could not be forgotten for it feeds the body of spirit as blood feeds the body of life.

If this was all there was to know, then it would surely be richer an understanding than any treasure of man could equal. But through all this came the most startling revelation of all: the power of insight extended all around a spirit, to the past, the present and to beyond, to places as yet unseen and ways as yet not taken. For if not there – the future – then where was I to go?

I felt a fatherly restraint lay upon me as a hand to steady a racing pulse. My father's words were clear:

*

'To call upon the past to give freely of its place in the future, is reliant upon the rightful cause of the present.'

*

For reasons of faint purpose, I had been too hasty to assume possession of these powers. Such gifts are not to be called upon at liberty. They are not responsive to desire or any thought of vestment in self-worth. To call upon the past, there must first be a balance between motive and necessity, it is insufficient to want to master the natural order of things. Just as spirits agree to give and receive of one to the other, so must the long-stilled trails of the past be prised from their forefathers by dint of true and worthy claim. Without such cause there is no power, no gift, and no knowledge; neither is there any awareness of their absence, for to be without knowledge is to condemn understanding to the dim light of observation alone.

The gift of calling is both delicate and sparingly evoked. Although robust and lasting in its history, and undoubtedly powerful, it is fragile in its execution and interpretation. That is how it has always been known, as a calling from the past and an invocation to the future. It is delicate because not all spirits have known this gift and those that have do not always find what they expect, or interpret what they find in a way that is appropriate to their situation. However, that is the nature of a gift that is sensitive to the inexact interpretation of shadowy reflections of layer upon layer of spiritual legacy and intertwined trails of spiritual endeavour; it should be accepted as a part of a picture and not the whole canvas.

*

My father had steadied my eagerness to rush to a conclusion beyond my grasp. Again, his words had taken the place of my own, as though to steer safe passage. I returned briefly to the birth of two worlds and the embodiment of spiritual plasma into the congealing mass of the new order. From that point, spirit was immersed into the unfolding natural geologies and then, later, through these vestiges of the First Way into the material edifices of humanity and life. All such landscapes and life forms contained, and will always contain, the essence of those lost spiritual elders. Lost from the First Way they may have been, but their unbroken alliance with matter was enough to allow future trails of passing spiritual presence to be recorded within the material landscape, to be heeded in turn by the next and all subsequent passing spirits. This store of energy, for that is what spirits leave as a legacy of their passing, is as a sensuous collage of signs and signals that can be interpreted as readily as any guide to the spiritual past. It can be dimmed by the passage of time and frosted by the intrusion of many later overlays and dramatic invasions of forceful intensity, but it is, nonetheless, a valuable source of a place's historical ambiance and spiritual inheritance. In many ways, it is the spiritual equivalent to history, except that it is a history that can be revisited and replayed from the present without the distortion of time.

I was intrigued by my father's description of this power of calling as connecting the future with the past through the present spirit. As with the Third Way, it was a bridge and the pivotal balance between physical and metaphysical worlds; it acted as a link between two halves of a distant reality. However fragile this coupling may be, it was an act conjured from the seeds of the past to reveal something of the present. It also appeared to be the outcome of unconscious behaviour, as though stemming from a will within the mind of spirit itself. Was it a will within a will, guarding the mind of a physical being? Once more, I was confused.

*

'Conscious behaviour is the unpredictable son of mortal senses, whereas the instinctive, unconscious behaviour of calling is the trusted kinsman of spiritual understanding.'

*

A fickle ally is no real friend, and so it is with the conscious act of understanding. We are what we know and can be as no other, be we mortal beings or spirit. To not accept our limitations is to deny the possibility of an existence beyond our comprehension and to wander in the bleak, dark isolation of our mind. The mortal mind sees only from within and is constrained by the limits of the senses to reach beyond the realm of self-imposed boundaries, whereas for a spirit there is no sight to wonder at, no sound to explain or touch to question. What comes to a spirit comes not as sensation to interpret but as truth to acknowledge. The truth that says to mankind: 'You are, therefore you exist,' says to spirit: 'You are so all else can be.'

The foot that leaves its mark does so without explanation, but within that mark is the undeniable truth of its presence: a traveller passing leaves a trail of its presence to be absorbed into creation's fabric. It is this bequest from the past to the present which is later revealed to the future. Just as an animal senses the smell of another, so a spirit recalls the presence of its past by the signature of its passing: the threads of life are woven into the tapestry of all matter. What I referred to as spiritual will is not the fanciful nature of mortal mind, it is the truth that is recovered – without question – from the past to guide the spirit in the present. Spirit is the unconscious part of mortal consciousness; it does not have a will, that belongs to the self-full nature of life. Spiritual unconsciousness is collective; it is of common origin and purpose; it is consistent and unfailing, but it is not omnipotent. Spirits can only influence behaviour in mortal beings by nature of their cohabitation and insight; a spirit is no more than the inner voice in an imperfect world that was itself born from imperfection.

*

'Who are we to visit our ways upon the new order?'

*

It seemed as though another page had turned. I had been presented with a fresh insight into the veil that guarded the secrets of immortal reason and its place in the mind of humankind.

But, if I was not mistaken my father had for the first time posed a question. It hung awkwardly between us, not as one awaiting a response, but rather in contemplation of its own imponderability to rest for a moment upon the wing of flight.

It was, I felt, a truth that was tantalizingly presented: complete yet distant, within reach, only to fade when about to be grasped. Something had been given and something had been offered up for wonder, of that I was sure. I had awoken and the flight of the multitude that had flown before urged me onwards.

If light is knowledge, then there must be a growing light surrounding a spirit as it unconsciously radiates its collective understanding to all in its name. From a common view of the past, I thought it would be a small matter to use that light to pierce the darkness and to illuminate the unreachable truths to come. After all, as my father had said, the past is the making of the future and a spirit believes in the eternity of existence as though, in itself, it was a sufficiency of evidence. Unquestioning immortal endeavour, collective unconsciousness, the sharing of insightful truths, the absence of self-full reason: all this is enough to acknowledge a spirit's sacrifice to a fuller reality and a belief that mortal life too has its part to play in this greater whole.

If this was so, and the future waited upon the past, then it could be foreseen through the past, and through the collective unconsciousness of spirit, known in the present too. Spirits relived the past to know the future. They had no need of question.

Why, therefore, had my father spoken thus: 'Who are we to visit our ways upon the new order?' If this was not a question then it was an answer. I sought not an answer but a question to his answer; or, could it be my father had posed a riddle?

'Who are we?' That was easy, we are spirit. 'Who are we to visit?' Could it be that I was to visit another place – the future? 'Who are we to visit our ways?' By this, my father would mean that I was to take the ways of spirit to some place ... to the new order? I was to go as spirit to the new world? If that was right, my father had answered *my* question: for if not there – the future – then where was I to go? It seemed as though I, as spirit, would come to know a future in the new world in some way as yet untold. But to know that I was to exist again, with a conscionable purpose, was as welcome a revelation to the meanderings of a benighted mind as any first light of dawn would be to the spiralling circles of a conundrum caught in the thermals of its own dark inscrutability.

The question is, of course, the very same that has been resting below the surface of mortal consciousness ever since life confronted the certainty of order. Change and the detachment from the everlasting truth of existence was the price paid for freedom and independence. What was lost became forgotten and what was known became insufficient to explain its essential nature. As life requires its counterweight, so too death becomes known as closure to all that has been left unanswered. It remains for spirit to seek what life has not been able to answer; the veil that covers the way of tomorrow is forever a guardian to the final truth. The question as to what lies beyond is one that will continue to be asked as long as there is life; for without hope of a future, there would be an impoverishment of mind and the decay of spirit. The light of understanding would truly fade into the bleakness of eternal darkness, and the spectre of nothing would come again as the consequence of failure.

My father did not contradict my musings. Belief in something beyond the nature of the present is at the heart of living and the essential core of spirit. This power, this spiritual ability is a tantalising glimpse of something yet to come, already written into destiny as sure as anything can be should the paths and ways trod not be modified. A plan it is, but not foretold by some higher source or compiled by some external observer, it is one of our own making, one that marks each step, each turn taken and each frontier crossed. All we have to do to see where we are headed is to look at the marks – the signs and signals, the doubts, the hopes, the energy, and the force of will that is left behind at each choice offered in the fabric of surrounding matter. This plan is not something tangible – it cannot be seen, but it can be known through our senses by the indelible marks left upon us, both within and without the mortal body, by choices made. And as we pass through the material world, so we in turn leave these marks for those who follow to read. We ourselves are both part and observer of this plan.

The Fullness of it all

MATTERS OF FUTURE PLANS and roles to come settled upon me as some already written prospect awaiting my attention. It was true that I had no insight into what lay ahead, in which respect I was no different from before, but I did have an inner certainty that I belonged to a much greater story than mine alone. My commitment to reason was no longer in question. I had been awakened to distant convictions of some nobler purpose, but to subvert the inventiveness of life and the power and authority of existence to some predetermined appointment in destiny is to deny the monadic omnipotence and magnificence of the Masterful Author of all things. What had been born from chance had been nurtured by spirit to allow the course of life to respond to change. All this was evidence that the manifestation of power in life had come from eternal providence – not as some rigid script to be enacted by demand, but as a means to enable all beings to respond freely to change within a repertoire of ever-expanding possibilities. Such freedoms were for life to explore and spirits to nurture until the final act was done and another play was written.

My future, I thought, *was* ordained, but only insofar as the future of life is ordained as death. How that comes about is a matter of part to be played and choice to be made.

*

'You are what you have always been ...' interrupted my father, with – if it were possible for me to feel from his embrace – a smile around each word, '... curious and fanciful by your own admission but never the lesser for it. Be comfortable in your deliberations and enquires and do not shy away from the fullest account you need from me. I had not intended to alarm you or to deceive you as to the sanctity of this place.

It is true that a spirit's reason for being is, as you say, to protect life – all life. But if you recall, it is through balance that this is to be achieved. For life to continue there must be an equilibrium between it and the life-giving energies that sustain its existence. Your journey is not yet over. There are new beginnings to come, no doubt, but it is not a spirit's role to judge what life has to offer. It is the spiritual legacy, first and above all else, to protect and sustain all its forms, not by command, as of old, but by influence and guidance. It is life that is so prone to weakness that our ancestral spirits had to fuse with matter to ensure a dynasty of control over it. It is the very commandments of existence that spirit upholds in order that being can be fulfilled. It is not for spirit to protect the moral order of life. Life is transitory, but it can conjure change and reorder the balance of nature in a moment. It is life that is the reason why spirit has embraced its many forms.'

We had begun a conversation. I had grown, and for the first time I responded with an avowal of my father's teachings.

'I know that the second rule can be no less important than the first. It sets out the means by which the first is to be achieved and is therefore subservient to it. The only recourse a spirit has to right a wrong or balance change is influence. A spirit cannot command or organise, it has no army to call upon, and for the most part it is alone and accountable to none other than the manner of its ancestors. It is not the nature of spirit to question its creed. In a way, a spirit is life itself, but it is free of all life's necessities and temptations to distinguish itself from any other. It is a central assembly of energy and power, a core of existence that protects and balances all matter. Spirit is bound by the essence of its being to balance change and maintain harmony just as it is to protect and sustain all life. The two codes are inseparable and forever given to serve.'

*

I had known my father as I knew my own thoughts, and now I knew the place of both in the role of a spirit. I was chastened and humbled by the shallowness of the waters in which life sought its way, but I was also buoyed by what I learnt about the gift of discerning events beyond the range of mortal imagination. As easily as we had come together, so we separated – without provision or resolve, alert or effort, there was a release and an acknowledgement of sufficiency that drew the fusion to a close.

My father had brought me to the very crux of the relationship between body and spirit. We had shared each other's presence in a way that I later realised had prepared me for what was to come. Certainly, this was not as spirit coexisting within the body, but it was a union from which I drew much understanding and one which in due course would be shown as a turning point in the way spirit interacted with life.

I could now understand my father when he said that events were not fully run. This was why my father was with me and taking so much care in my tutoring. It was he, after all, who had alerted me so dramatically to the pending dangers that day on the fell, so that together we two might succeed in offering Christian insight to the future, a future that must have been so clear to my father as to cause him such pain upon a blind rejection. I recall my own anguish at Christian's denial and my distraction with the increasingly heavy darkness around me that seemed to sap my energy and mock my isolation. It was this that conspired against me to thwart my father's warning. It was this subversion of spiritual resolve and suppression of 'right-doing' that I now saw as belonging to a premeditated plan, and if that was true then Christian's destiny that day was already written in all that was around me. My sense of foreboding on that occasion had been well-founded. I had been given a tantalising insight into the future but had failed to prevail upon the mortal Christian, or to induce an alliance with Douglas's spirit, to contest fate and defeat the conspiracy against us.

I now believed that there had been a great wrong inflicted upon Christian that day. It was not solely due to misfortune or the frailties of man or spirit. There had been a collusion of ill against us, and my father's foretelling that all was not yet done was persuading me that I had some further part to play. Exactly what and how this might be, I could not imagine, but I felt sure that there was not to be a swift conclusion to this journey.

I felt as close to my father as I had ever done, as he continued with his guidance.

*

'Your path on that day had been trodden before.'

*

Both Douglas and I had taken that journey on previous occasions only to return unsuccessful – as we would have then had it – from the pursuit of our goal. But, as a spirit I had been successful in averting what was to eventually overtake me and result in the end of my physical life. The positive nature of the marks left on these earlier visits would have been noted by those conspiring against us. They would have been used to increase their forces so that on the final journey we were oppressed and often disorientated by the sheer weight of malevolence. At this point I was aware of the likely outcome, and it was

I who called my father for assistance and not the other way around. He appeared to Christian through me, as an apparition portending a fateful future, but despite the alarm – which was without question known and touched, if only fleetingly, the deepest most instinctive mortal impulse to survive – there was a confusion of conscionable doubt and forceful delusion that combined to deny its existence and dismiss the verity of the warning. This was not a battle of equals. The chains that shackle the behaviour of spirits are not so applied to the forces of disruption. They are free of constraint and commandment; they are not bound by conscience or threatened by justice; they have no fear of wrong or regard for right; they do not forgive error or pardon failure, neither do they respect strength or excuse weakness. It is the weak who are their prey and the strong who are their enemy. These forces are spirits too, but they have never been a part of life and have therefore never returned to the spirit world at the end of life. They have existed in the new world since its creation, but unlike those whose destiny was to evolve with matter into life, these spirits were released into the wastes and tides of eternal suspension to remain soulless and desolate without commandment or cause to control and direct their energy. It is yet again further evidence of the flawed nature of creation when so much was lost through change.

*

'There is no other account of it, but do not mistake that these are still spirits.'

*

I knew that spirits do not know evil and cannot by themselves commit evil; it is not in their spiritual heritage to do so. These soulless, vacant forces roam as unruly and restless energy to unwittingly disrupt and hinder all aspects of life. It is not until they are brought together as a group and given a direction or purpose that they can become a potent force for malevolent intent. For this to happen they need a dominant influence, something that will focus their irritating, impish behaviour into a more controlled and aggressive nucleus about which to spin. They need leadership. Spirits such as these, alone in the free world, are not capable of concerted action or any form of communication between themselves. Neither do spirits, in general, communicate directly with each other, for this would require them to divert their energy away from their physical host and their duty to it. There are exceptions, of course, where the wellbeing or survival of their host requires a spirit to seek assistance, but more often than not that is a calling to the past, rather than to the present. The behaviour of these lost spirits can be harnessed by a particularly strong power, such as that flowing from a deranged mind or even from a particularly forceful or determined will. It is not the source that is significant, but the strength and intensity of the emotions or will that attracts and captures the wandering spirit. The need for purpose is embedded and fused in the spiritual legacy. We are all easily led, and at times misled, on a path that deviates from our undertakings. On occasion we can be so far from our undertaking that recovery is long and passes through more than one lifetime to disrupt our future beyond the reach of the original erring.

My father had been slowly laying the pieces before me and allowing me to place them in order so that at each stage I could come to my own conclusions as to the unfurling of this chain of events. I knew so much yet could not bring myself to draw the final lesson.

*

'Remember, do not search for an explanation and do not seek to apportion blame or indulge in recrimination.'

*

I was not to seek justice through penance or retribution; it is the way of it and cannot be undone. All I had been asked to do was to know the fullness of all that had happened before concluding where my path might lead in the future.

My father had checked my deliberations in mid-thought before I could arrange all that I had been shown as the cradle for my conclusions. It was true that I was about to look for what lay within, rather than that in which it must lie. My father's interruption was a way of guiding my attention back to the fullness that surrounds all that takes place and from which such potent actors engage and influence each turn of destiny.

It would be necessary to place the last by the deeds of the first, and thereby all those in-between in turn.

Only then would I be in a position to justly deliver my conclusion.

In many ways, this sense I had of a cradle in which to lay my discoveries was appropriate to my journey so far. I was about to experience the uneasy flush of wonder at awakening from a comfortable womb of immaculate intention where all false idols had been shielded from me. My unworldly innocence was to be laid in a bed of worldly imperfection where ideals would be tempered and justice tested by a confusion of competing persuasions of right and wrong.

Just as I have likened my start on this journey to the point at which my father infused me with the conception of two worlds, so now I was about to be born again from the seed of both and confronted with the realities of different and distinct perspectives on life. Yes, it was the fullness of everything, the absolute account of matters. But this was only an inset to existence and that continuation was still to come.

Just as before, once I had acknowledged the way of it and made the commitment to accept the truth as it was shown to me, I was relieved of the distraction of doubt. This time there was no great revelation or joyous fulfilment upon which I could rely as evidence of enlightenment, but I can attest to the clarity of mind and resolve of purpose that intensified a receptiveness to what my father referred to as 'the fullness of it all'. I was in no doubt that I was charged with rationalising all that I had come to know through my spiritual tutoring, with all that I had been and known as real to deliver a single account of what was already recorded on the pages of my life. I was obliged to confront both realities in my search for the truth.

I had no wish to recall the fact of my physical death, neither had I need to recall the image that carried me from the finality of one life back to the eternity of another; but as Christian once was, so too was I to return again to that moment.

*

I knew the hand that released me was not guided by my own will, and the force that plagued me that day was not a shadow of my imagination. Sight, I had learnt, was not the sole witness to reality. But what was absent from my understanding was the means by which all this concluded as it did. I had no measure of cause, and that which I was about to propose would have been false and so was taken from me by my father's interruption.

Whether I was taken to a new reality or whether it came to me, I do not know, but I was central to it. I was the point, the nucleus around which all that had taken place and everything that was to be known was released to flow through me with the freedom that comes from a pledge of confession from all involved. There was a flood of understanding that began with as deliberate a sense of certainty as I have ever known. I was taken to the end of one thing and then to the end of another, and another, until I was so far from the first as to have no sight or knowledge of it. Yet, I was where I was because of it and could not have been there without having come from it.

The simplicity was undeniable. I knew my place, but to know how I came to it I would have to return to the first by going back through each end in turn until I came to the last, which would now be the first and the goal of my understanding. I could not – it was made clear to me – return any other way if the fullness of my quest was to be accomplished.

The journey was not mine alone. There were others whose paths I shared and ways I crossed and from whom I would give and take, and for a while rest with – until their path and mine would divert and lead each to its own end. Through all this came a growing certainty with the placing of things in order, not of time or sequence of progression – for there were many overlays, many competing values and perspectives that would each intrude upon a way not yet run or a mind not yet set – but in destiny: that order of certainty that diminishes all possible outcomes to a diminishing number of probable fortunes through the conscious actions of a determined mind. It is these, the defining steps taken that slowly seal our fate. Just as it had been with Christian, where events so profoundly intruded upon life, so it was to be with me as his spirit, to lay bare the path taken so that I might know the better what lay ahead and what it was I was being asked to do.

*

I now knew something of Douglas's past too; for, as I had traversed back through one lifetime, so I had touched him on more occasions than I had thought possible. The turns of fate and fortune that weave a thread to leave trails of past deeds in amongst the pattern of mortal lives, also revealed something of the life of those encountered along the way. I found that in knowing, there is understanding and sympathy for a soul overtaken by events so lightly under his control, and that blame and recrimination served me no purpose. But there was more to it yet. My own role in all this was not beyond reproach. As a spirit, I had protected and nurtured Christian's spiritual conscience in a way that I thought was both compatible with the spiritual code and conducive to the more instinctive and self-serving laws of nature. I had set free his powers of imagination and encouraged his more sombre, reflective nature by, at times, suppressing the flow of conscionable direction between us – I had relinquished the role of guardian to spiritual fidelity to allow contemplation free rein in order that this might deepen the process by which truly momentous and possibly fateful decisions are made. Whilst I thought this to be a worthy means of education, it had turned out to carry a degree of detachment between mind and spirit that eventually led to a more deliberate and rational denial of the spiritual sense of foreboding that passed between us on that final journey. Further still, it was now incumbent upon me to recognise that this state of obliviousness to spiritual guidance was by no means limited to Christian. It was at the root of all that took place that day.

Now, I was charged with acknowledging the task before me. There was to be the opportunity to make amends and turn this injustice to some betterment that would return the balance between the spiritual and physical codes.

One further requirement was made of me. I had been taken to an end and knew it to be that which I had known as life in the physical world. But this was not the end of life itself. I was not given any sense of what was to come, but there was a certainty of something more. It was this unfolding that brought with it a realisation that what lay ahead would continue to play upon the past so that what I sought could only be what my father had referred to as the 'fullness' of it and not, as I had supposed, the truth.

This lure of many endings, both within and at the very end of all life, was to have a significant effect on my perception of truth and reality. At this point, I believe that the truth had suddenly been stolen from me and my notion of reality was disappearing along with it. I had been shown a sense of certainty that was to cradle my inspection and deliberations, but now the verity of that was under attack by the notion that there could be no absolute conclusion, no final judgement until all had passed and been taken into account.

That rock of belief that had always been behind the presence of truth had been taken from me. If such understanding can only be found at the last, at the very end when everything that was is gone and everything that was to have been is lost from sight, where then does truth lie? It lies waiting: waiting within all matter, waiting for the moment when it is called to declare the beginning of a greater sorrow; too late that dawn of certainty that reveals the frailty of character that is blind to the guidance from within. The truth will be known up to the point when existence is stilled, infinity rests, and memory is lost.

There is nothing that can be known after that point, for it is within matter that the Book of Life is recorded. At the end of everything there will be no witness, and all that ever was will return from whence it came. As we are not yet ended then we cannot be at that point, we cannot know the whole truth as that requires we know the end as we know the beginning. We can therefore only approach the truth through a process of discovery to realise the fullness of reality – that which is, before what is to come has made itself known.

The next may always be the last, in which case the fullness of reality would be very close to the truth; in fact, all there is to know, short of that final moment that would tell the reason behind that one last act and thereby all in turn before it. Such a moment may only be imagined, for it would be as infinity overtook it and cast all into perpetual oblivion. Truth is an enviable concept only approachable by degrees. All that we see and know is true only in the fullness of that which has gone before.

I had already been required to give up my illusions of life as the first step in shedding personal persuasions of truth. Now I was being asked to lay that cleansed mind in this newfound place, which was no longer to be called truth. Thus, I came to see the wisdom of my father's words when he asked no more of me than to see the fullness of all that surrounded my final moments. I was to know the truth only so far as it was possible to know the past. I was to know how one thing changes another and will continue to change what had been known and held as true.

What started as a casual acquaintance with the

many excursions in life had grown into an intimate understanding of the most purposeful expedition ever undertaken. But the disclosure of one is only a part and this was to be no singular account. All those whose ways shared or crossed the chosen path were called on to give their view. There was no omission or deed left unvisited. Each step was ordered and set with meaning. Memory, I discovered, is a weak and fickle recorder, prone to embellishment and obstruction to avoid the distant goal. I saw events from afar without prejudice or favour to person or place. The remit of my inspection was broad and encompassed many perspectives. I visited all quarters and all recesses to uncover each connection, one to the next, until all that was to know became known. The last was met and I lay safely in Mother Earth's womb. If my life had been a journey of discovery and wonder, then this search for fullness had surely been the pinnacle of its reason. The pieces were all but in place.

*

Just as I had once seen but never known my father, so too had I been stone-eyed to Douglas. I had been blinded by sight, and it was not until I had been freed from the ties of the physical senses that I was able to free my spiritual insight to lay alongside the images of physical life. It was as if I were bringing together an overlay of all that had been seen and all that was left unseen to expose the completeness of being.

The forces that massed around us that day were not

attracted to me, as I had begun to fear, but to Douglas. It was he who was weakened, thus providing the conduit through which such forces took their lead. It was Douglas's imbalance of mortal strength and frailness of spirit that commanded their attention. It was his motive that was the stronger, and it was he who steered the events to their conclusion. There were four and not two in the gully that day: two mortal beings and two immortal spirits, of which one was now aligned with the quarrelsome energy that fed on the self-doubt plaguing my mortal self. Douglas, his spirit, and Christian were awkwardly acting in concert with the forces that fed on the absence of spiritual fortitude.

If Douglas was the channel through which this ill-intent flowed, then Christian was the vessel that bore the load. It was he who was the weaker of the two in his capacity to place himself above the call of others when defending the certitude of his feelings. He was in awe of his surroundings and distracted by the desecration of the object of his wonder. He was afraid.

But, I too played a part, for it was I, as spirit, who was so overtaken by the weight and growing ferocity of energy in the narrow confines of the gully, that I was rendered powerless to deflect their intent by any means that might have diverted Christian from his course. All his physical energies had been focused on the demands of his quest to match, or at least draw close to, the greater skills of his friend. There was also the distraction of the schism between him and Douglas over his intuitive respect for the glory about him. All this was a disturbance to his mind and a barrier that excluded any possibility of retreat or spiritual guidance from the moment that Douglas began the final climb out of the gully.

As the actors were laid bare before me, so I was to place them, without prejudice, in the wider pageantry of many events that were not of their making; for it was the culmination of many previous journeys, often beset by sorrows of their own, that finally coalesced into the wretched conclusion. Wretched it was, for as often occurs in situations where no authority or cardinal purpose prevails, the outcome was not as intended.

The forces that so idly conspired to disrupt order had sensed a weakness in the bond between body and spirit, between mind and resolve. They had unmercifully pitted contrasting characteristics, one against the other, on an occasion that tested each to its limits. It was only at the very last that these malicious forces had revealed their hand. What happened was the inevitable conclusion of disorder, a medley of unguided energy and freedom, a collision of occasion and choice. There had been no deliberate act of malice. Christian was the casualty of creation. Had it not been for that first, unrecorded lapse of control in the First Way, such imbalances in harmony and order would not exist and the fragile nature of life would be unknown.

Instead, the unintended consequence of that day was the imbalance between mortal endeavour and spiritual reason; one acted against the other, oblivious of the feebleness of each without the other. The tension that exists between the conscious deliberations of life and the unconscious callings of spirit, had been enacted in isolation of wise counsel and amid a great malaise of purpose. It was an occasion of vacancy filled with unguided intent. It was injustice that was to frame what followed and set the course for the rest of my journey.

Much later I would come to realise the deeper significance of this whole episode. This was not just reparation for a wrong, nor was it an expression of my own growing belief that there was more to come from the duality of existence between body and spirit. Unbeknown to me, this was a tipping point in the spiritual ethos. The conduct allowable to fulfil long-embedded characteristics of spiritual existence was about to be challenged. The balance between the two worlds was carried heavily by spirits, and it was now necessary to explore other ways of sharing this load. I was unwittingly lending myself to the start of another chapter in the metamorphosis of spiritual resourcefulness.

I returned slowly to the reassuring occupation of my father's presence and his right to know my innermost thoughts. We shared a long, reflective silence, content and sure as any picture painted under the patronage of a benevolent master. I knew the pleasure of my thoughts spoken by another.

*

'We have come a long way together and you have understood much of what has taken place to bring about change and the preservation of life. As you now understand, the weight of the past bears heavily on the future and the legacy of all our actions outlasts their consequences. Such a disturbance to the delicate balance of harmony can create opportunities for idle forces to exploit a weakness from which arteries of disorder can flow to erupt and create further dislocation until all sight of the first is lost in a confusion of cause and remedy. It is now your calling to make amends in some way, to arrest this transgression before further turmoil ensues. From this end will come new beginnings. The story will continue from where you left it, but the course will change. This book, which is already so full, is never closed and can never be finished.'

*

My father was taking leave of me and I knew not whether we would share each other's presence again. The dullness I once felt from the absence of his fellowship was no longer with me. I could only express in return all the goodwill that was streaming into me as I slowly faded from his world.

Matamorphosis

LIFE MAY BE SAID to be a presence within a single greater entity that encompasses both being and existence.

As to the questions of truth and the future beyond life: I now knew that they extended to a world beyond physical realities, where the Eternal Spirit strives to conduct life to fulfill its meaning within the wider monadic expression of everything. As for the truth – once extolled as the supreme virtue – it is no more than the fullness of reality, only to be found in the future after life has had its say.

That life does not appear to represent anything other than a series of accidental expressions colliding in self-willed contrariness is enough to suggest it has yet to find its place within the monadic divinity of which it is a part. It has no collective role beyond the compass of its being, merely a myriad of mixed excursions into false delusions of its station.

If the future were to take its lead from the past, then such experimentation would continue to the point where life's turn would come to its end. When death releases the spirit, it too is restrained within the confines of its world. It is not possible for spirit to recreate itself or to cease its being; it is as an ocean replenished by lives lost and drained by evaporation. As with an ocean, so is spirit whole, it is of one body, one mind, and one thought; it is indivisible, cleansed by its power, its uniformity, and completeness. It is not possible to extract a single part from the whole; when it is distilled to dwell in life, it remains as that from which it came, but now it is bound once more to the laws and limits of its new calling. In all this ebb and flow, it never loses the essence of its being to infuse life with the sense that it has come from something more than itself.

Boundaries and the curtailment of reality will forever be a part of life. Life comes from life, and life comes from the end of life, too, as death releases one expression of being to the next. The spiritual centre is the equivalent to life in the physical world, except in the one small detail that is to separate life from existence: it is eternal. The Eternal Spirit was there at the beginning and will remain at the end. As one passage of life passes to release another, so the spiritual memory of it will fade to be replaced by the certainty of ages that is locked in the collective unconsciousness of spiritual waters.

The role of spirit is unending, but within its many physical manifestations and lifetimes, there are numerous conclusions to its part and no simple rules as to when one should draw to a close and another begin. Christian's role was over, but what was to take place in his name was far from usual. Certainly, his life was ended, but the circumstances of his death, the ill-conceived intrusion of unfettered spirits, and worse, the memory of abandoned hope in the final instant that released him from the slender line that anchored him to life, was anathema to spiritual creed and commandment.

It was this last act of helpless complicity that compelled spirit to redress an imbalance which would, if left unchecked, threaten the course of a greater assembly: one greater convergence of two disparate forms into a united concourse to advance the goal of being to a way beyond the realms of mortal or spiritual endeavour alone. This was *not* normal, not a small matter at all, and ultimately not attributable to Christian or Douglas; in that alone, it was something that was bound to happen sooner or later.

*

It, therefore, came as no surprise that I should find myself once again surveying all that had been so familiar to me. I recognised my surroundings, not as physical features or distinctive shapes of recent acquaintance, but as warm images of pleasant occasions; in the same way as I had first heard my father's voice, there was a familiarity as intense as any physical sense could evoke, and I was enveloped in the majesty of landscape that thrilled and touched every part of me. At first, the detail of it escaped me, but the freshness, the expanse of it all contrasted with the closure and intensity of the containment I had just left. What lay before me seemed full of opportunity and wonder, and for the moment I could not help but bask in the delight of my return to the world I had once believed to be the sole expression of everything possible. Where before I had seen beauty, I now saw the masterful hand of spiritual care and nurture of patient endeavour; where I had once seen a pageant of colour and texture, I now saw the fullness of creation and the delicate artistry of change. There was a new depth to my observation so that I felt and knew more of all that flowed through the essence of my being than I had ever done before. I saw with the acuteness of an eagle's eye and knew more than any sage or scholarly historian could ever tell. The freshness of air was as a cloak to my presence and, although I had no need of either, I passed across the land, once so dear to me, as lightly as any one of the gently falling snowflakes around me.

My complete knowledge and presence of this place was as natural to me as returning blood is to the heart; I knew I was no longer the embodiment of life, but I was the unworldly accompaniment by which it existed. I remained as a means to life even when there was none, and all that had changed was as little as takes place in the space between heartbeats. As spirit, I had always known what had been awakened within me, but it was life that had stilled much of what I knew and life that required so much from me to protect and nurture its ways. I was here to right a wrong and in some small way to restore a sense of equilibrium to a passage of events that had subverted justice and threatened the spiritual code.

*

Once again, I knew Douglas. Just as before, with his arms flailing he half-ran, half-skated across the frozen crown of Dale Head and away from the agonies of the gully to start the descent back down to the valley. His progress over the sculpture of the white body-torso was as careless to his welfare as anything could be. The sureness of foot and elegance of stride was replaced by the most graceless passage that can be imagined. He appeared as one frantic, devoid of all-purpose, plagued and pursued by the horrors of a hallucinatory mind. This I knew was not so; rather, he was enveloped by the most hideously grotesque shadows imaginable. This was no impish mischief or casual flight of thuggery, it was as cold a cohort of wretchedness as ever stalked this land, lacking in control as any frenzied feeding pack on its prey. There was no accounting for the intensity of the throng as it swarmed in contrasting darkness to the whiteness around. There was no steady shape or form to this mass, and to size the magnitude would be as to ask the tally of waves in a storm at sea, serving only to disguise the effect and lessen the threat of the whole. This was not a coalition of numbers; this was energy in its rawest, most bitter state. The same energy that had surrounded me in the gully had multiplied in its intensity and become inured to its own fetid bile to such a degree that its hunger was insatiable. It had turned inward on the very source that had first attracted its spite.

I resolved to draw nearer. As he came to the saddle that would lead to lower ground, I could sense his helplessness grow within him; he paused, as if in some deep effort to regain his composure before descending the treacherous drop over the saddle's side and down the boulder-strewn narrows of the frozen beck. I knew, as he did, how deceiving the blanket of snow could be in concealing the nooks and crannies so craftily set to swallow the unwary sheep or unsteady traveller. The beck's friendly chuckle as it tossed and teased its way around the dark recesses was no longer there to prevent the hasty step or incautious leap; how he must have wished for the comfort available from the probing of a trusted staff. If he but had the presence of a rational mind, he too must have dwelt on the wretched sequence of events that had spiralled to such tragedy from so innocent a day's beginning.

This, however, was not the delay of one carefully considering his options; it was more the act of a despairing mind weighing up the fateful choice of two evils. The descent would be testing for two, even with rope and staves, but for one, with neither aids nor companion, it would be both dangerous and slow, so slow that he would have plenty of time to dwell on his own part in the day's events: his earlier insistence that they should go on, his refusal to listen to caution, and his flawed belief in his own ability to protect a weaker partner. It was his responsibility as the stronger of the two not to exceed his friend's ability. Friend! What friend had he been when it really mattered? How would he explain his actions to Christian's mother? All these thoughts, these doubts, would be there to plague him if he were to allow it. The choice, if choice there was, had been made for him.

He took one step and, as if on a toboggan, plunged feet first onto the steepest part of the slope. For a moment he was free and ploughing a quickening furrow through the immaculate field of snow. The sudden release from the pressure around him was enough to lighten his expression as the sheer exhilaration of his bravado intensified his feelings. It was, however, only a momentary escape and even as the first flicker of pleasure touched the corners of his mouth, I heard the beginnings of the shrill wailings that had so haunted me in the gully.

*

As Douglas had leapt through the clean lines of the upswept overhang of the cornice that so gracefully covered the normal rocky profile of the saddle, the gathered horde about him had wavered; his disappearance had for an instant evaded their attention, and, but for the lingering vapour of terror in his wake, things may have been different. But, as they regained the scent and swarmed with renewed vigour in his passage, I could sense the telltale hand of fate descend on the diminishing figure below me.

*

The skittish cackling of the disturbed frozen crusts of snow as they scattered across the shattered glaze of the surface around him was overtaken by a deeper, ominous crack and reverberating groan. First one, then another slab of compacted snow was dislodged from beneath him to leave him surfing in a cold sea of surging white crests and foaming troughs of powder. What little control he had

had on his descent was now subsumed by a greater will. His path was unnaturally deflected, as though compelled by some fateful urge, towards the very crags where in days past we had polished and paraded our burgeoning skills. In a muffled cry of pending fate, and much as a fly would be whisked from the presence of some irritable dignitary, Douglas was cast loose over the edge of a rocky precipice and onto the lessening slope and softer snows below. As the following arc of snow closed over him, I watched as swirling shadows performed their graceless flight of victory over the spot at which he sank beneath the settling white stillness above.

As dark and tempestuous as it was in that moment as Douglas disappeared beneath the snow, immediately after came a peace that belied the enormity of what had taken place. The marauding hordes dispersed as readily as they had assembled as if refuting their very existence. What purpose they had was gone and their fragile cohesion was dashed as they faded from the source of their attraction. It was as though all the energy in that place had been subsumed for some forbidden purpose, and now that it was over there was nothing left with which to lament its passing. There was no sighing breeze, no cleansing sound of water, and no sign of life to bear witness. Nature had played an unwitting part in the proceedings and was now helpless to change the outcome.

The cycle of life had once again drawn to a close. The returning prospect of yet another gift being stolen, so casually as to deny the generosity, love, and care invested in its conception and nurture, was as painful to my newfound sensibilities as any loss of self-worth could be to a rejected lover's heart. It was as though the very pulse of creation had stopped to question its place in the heavens.

*

All life is precious, it comes from a single seed; this intensity of experience for one was no less for its smallness in number. What befalls one is carried by all as a mark of anguish. The peal of remorse tolls loud and weighs heavily on a spirit as the eternal bearer of ill-fortune for those born from the ashes of the First Way.

*

I waited for what I knew was to happen next. In so doing I felt the diminishing signs of life's energies evaporate from Douglas's entombed body; as the last faded, I knew his spirit as it departed from its physical form.

His was a spirit as lost as any can be in the aftermath of an unfolding tragedy. We each knew the presence of the other and we each knew our part, but unlike my encounter with the spirit of my father, this was in the mortal world and the passing of time was as a barrier between us. As the light of his spirit rose, I was drawn to the path of the departing energy and guided down through the diminishing spiral of life to the source of its being.

This action was involuntary and beyond my immediate explanation. I had no thought or plan, nor did I have the will to resist. The motion I experienced was as being carried across a cavernous void, one that was too wide to bridge and too deep to see, but nonetheless there in all its hidden depths and power to prohibit free passage. Although this was no physical obstacle, it was as durable an impediment to returning life as can be constructed from the recesses of a lowly imagination. In the realms of the physical world, all things must fade from existence, but this was not as something that would crumble or decay with time, this was an eternal monument to the mysteries of being: a barrier that would stand forever to guard the sanctity of universal understanding. This was a defining principle, a rule of creation that was mercifully suppressed to allow me, as Christian's spirit, to return to the physical world through the body of Douglas.

I had come again to life, through the very auspices of its origin, in such a way as to know its meaning in advance of its being. The monadic power that encompassed the First Way, that source of all spiritual and material being, which first embraced me in the isolation of death, now once again exercised its prerogative over the forces of life. This was not of my will. I had been granted freedom from the spiritual creed of many to follow a singular course in what was about to become an unprecedented intervention in the conduct of life

All this, although apparent to my circumstance, was hidden to me in a way that neither hindered nor ruled my step in what took place. I had been released to be more tightly embraced for it. Had it not been so, and had I but thought to dwell on the seemingly insurmountable impediments to the code of spiritual behaviour and the very actuality of spiritual existence, I surely would have hesitated and lost the moment. How it came to be that this particular play should spark the turn of hand to trigger the next phase of my journey is explicable only by the fact of its occurrence. It happened as it did because it could; it was once again, a question of time.

It was not as one that I acted that day, but as the instrument of one who had liberated spiritual sphere and mortal reach to reveal hitherto inconceivable heights of possibility. It was not miraculous intervention in the sense of an unexplained phenomenon, it was simply a prising apart of the limits to possibility. I had come to know the onset of both worlds as one in a duality of purpose in response to what had become a singularly painful expression of the weakness of one alone. The boundaries of opportunity had been breached, and the impediment of a lonesome mind relieved of its unequal struggle to make sense of the cause of such hurt and sorrow.

*

As I passed through the last vestige of departing spiritual energy, I felt the presence of Douglas's soul as it prepared to follow in the path of his spirit and return to place his account alongside all others in life. My presence alone was enough to check its departure. I became as Douglas – as intimate with the ways of his being as any conscionable thought could ever entertain.

If not physically dead already, Douglas was very close to his last breath. He had undergone considerable shock in the minutes since Christian's death and his life functions were inactive. He had, however, never been without spiritual energy and in that sense at least he had not been abandoned. I had no thought but to believe that spirit was life and that as long as there was spirit there would be life. I united with his soul, and in the full belief that we would rise together I passed my energy through my extended form to return life to a lifeless body.

A New Beginning

DOUGLAS RESPONDED WITH A pneumatic retch. His eyes, first shut to the horrors of wingless flight, remained ice-tight to shield his knowing the deathly cast of his inner-self staring back at him. His mind whirled between temples of burning numbness as it sought an explanation for his confinement. He gasped as the first shivering breath caught his lungs, and then again as the stuttering inhalations tumbled over themselves in a disorderly queue to quicken the pulse from his stubborn heart. He was alive. Stupidly alive, without sight, or limb to command, or body to feel. There was no order, no back or front, above or below; no place to go or means to know his corner. He was held in a merciless embrace as tightly as any orphaned mind caught in the denial of its existence.

He retched again, as his heart demanded more of him, and the surge of life pulsed through his veins as a reminder of its meaning. A trickle of saliva left in his mouth became his re-birth; it awoke him to the uneasy movement of spittle across his lips. He sucked on crystal breaths and bit on unseen snow as he tried to recover the fluids seeping from him. He choked as a modicum of the flow streaming out of him returned. He had found a meridian to his being.

Buried. The word stayed with him, tearing into his life, consuming his thoughts, defying belief, demanding he respond. He pictured 'up' for the first time, and squirmed in his cocoon to face this new zenith. Again, and again he twisted his head and tried to swallow, until at last, at the end of all possible contortion, he could swallow and breathe without choking. His effort was rewarded as the quickening of his heart brought a pulse to his body. He shivered. He focused on the small movements as they quivered through his limbs, his neck, shoulders, arms and hands – each beating with fresh energy striving to be free.

He became small and large in quick succession, contracting and expanding his body in time with his breathing, testing for a weakness in the folds that sought to restrain him. One finger stretched out to freedom, one hand reached for salvation; it was all relative to the struggle between body and mind.

As it happened, it was the middle finger on the right hand that first reconnected thought to movement and a newfound sense of what might just be possible. In the clutches of numbing senselessness, he had found a companion to his companionless existence. One finger, then another, pleading – cajoling a paralysed limb to awaken and come back to life. He willed his hand to push and claw up his thigh, to his waist, to his chest. He leaned, lost in the past, his shoulder bearing a sack of coke for his forge as he rocked back and forth feeling the flames lick his hand. He spat to gauge the temperature; cursing at the miserable hiss of kindle, he bit hard on his blackened finger as it brushed the phlegm from his mouth. The mixture of pain and the white taste of black dust was both sweet and sour as he played in a curious netherworld where a milky mist hides all horrors.

He recovered to the worst of all possible realities as clamped teeth slowly brought back the feeling to the knuckle in his mouth. His mind drew upon pain; he would not be beaten. He imagined the snow giving way, melting around him as the fire within compelled a passage be opened. He gauged his other hand to be behind his head; one leg below and the other in front, perhaps, but as yet unfixed in his mind. He was cast and laid in a pose of pitiful helplessness. As he stared unseeing at the darkened skin on the back of his finger, he felt one ... two ... three crystal crumbs of crushed snow fall onto the back of his hand like teardrops pleading for attention. He turned his unblinking gaze, as if to follow their course, until he could move no more. His eyes burned in their sockets and he choked, half-spitting, half-tearing his indented knuckle from his mouth. 'Up,' he whispered. It was the final prophecy; no matter how far he had to go, no matter how much a struggle, he would survive.

*

The day was bluer than he remembered. As he freed himself from the last tissues of his bindings, his movements were a colourless piece in a ghostly puzzle of misplaced times. His memory was blank. Whether by dread or degree of cold, he had no past to run from or future to run to; he was suspended in the clutches of pain and sorrow. All he knew was the biting chill and clinging grip of his awkward bed. He had been lying face down and had somehow come unwound from the turns of a nightmare to find himself trapped in its numbing aftermath of tangled fact and fiction. Even the parts of his body were separated from his command and seemed distant to his will. In truth, it was hard to tell what belonged to life and what did not, for the snow still clung to him as a cast of skeletal spores, reluctant to release him from his walled grave. All was white and still in a way so peaceful as to belie its dominance over life and form of whatever kind. It would have been easy to rest, to succumb to its intrusion upon his right to be different.

As he relaxed his struggle to reassemble the day's events into some meaningful pattern that might explain his situation, his breathing eased; he half-rolled and half-dragged himself out of his shallow tomb. He was surprised to see he had been buried in no more than four foot of snow and, as his vista broadened to the wider expanse of views, his orientation returned. His relief was short-lived. As he pounded the feeling back into his limbs, the slow awakening of his sensibilities drew the awful reality to the fore. For a while, the fight to survive had freed him from a darkness he had long carried; the absence of memory had lifted an oppression of mind from his consciousness that had dulled his waking hours and plagued his slumbers for many a year. The weight of responsibility for some inherited flaw had been cast aside and for once in his life he had been without the lingering air of reproach that had stalked him for as long as he cared to remember. But now, as the shades of a winter's day settled into a familiar horizon, the events of the preceding hours closed in upon him to drag him back to the clutches of reality.

'Oh, God! Oh, GOD! In GOD's NAME ...' The words escaped him with a violence that shook both him and the valley into life. *Oh God! ...God! ...God!* The echoing reply cruelly repeated his distress, lest in some small part he should forget the merest detail. His mind raced as the returning horrors screamed back into his consciousness. No, surely not! No! No, no this can't be true! He looked about him as though some part of this landscape would release his friend, free him from its grip as if to say: *A dream; you're right; we meant no ill.* The riven gullies perhaps, the bold crags, the high peaks, the low valley; he scanned them all for mercy and compassion. Each, in turn, hid from his gaze, retreated under his stare, and bowed its silhouette in shame from his enquiry. He wanted to turn – to run, to forget, to die where he was. There was to be no comfort.

A voice without sound, without knowledge of breath or the blood of life that moved him: 'Oh Christian ... Christian ... what have I done; *what* have I done.' Again, his words came back to him, as though on a sigh of despair; he knew, but had to be told. *He's gone ... gone!*

He turned. A solitary figure in a solitary place, without colour, passion, or visible sign of life. Both he and the landscape in which he stood were isolated from feeling and devoid of any sense of reason. Barren and bereft of comfort, charity or pity, it was as lonely a scene of silent remorse as any water stilled or birdsong hushed by winter's grip. All that he had found in this place had been taken from him in a way that reflected the much greater loss around him. The silence did nothing to stem the leaching of blood from the body of life.

Douglas's Story

*

The cloth that girded the man was as stiff and severe as any preacher's collar in the light of a pulpit's candle. It was as stepping into another's shoes and treading a path distant to the one that had brought me thus far. I, as Christian's spirit, knew the cast of character: the subtleties of emotion as they sprung unchecked from the fevers of the past; the colours of persuasion and the shades of belief as they rose from the canvas of life. In all, I absorbed the inner being that had crafted the outer mantle of the man.

*

For the Greater Good

DOUGLAS HAD BEEN BORN unwanted. The son of jarring seed scattered wildly one night to fend for itself from the very first cast.

It was in the early morning of the seventeenth day of December 1771 that Douglas entered the world. Forsaken of all but name – and that, only hurriedly bequeathed by his mother Rose in the admission's register of Liverpool Infirmary – he lay so still as to move the doctor to reflect that, as God was his judge, he had done his best, and if the boy was to be spared the eternal torment of his mother, then a minister was needed, without delay, to baptise the poor little bastard. On seeing the child and hearing the doctor's tale, the minister hastily christened the still, silent infant.

Daniel Douglas, son of Rose Douglas – lately departed from this world – had been admitted to his place in the order of creation. The final benediction that 'God be merciful to them both' was still to be found etched into his soul, lest time and the grip of his swaddling clothes should ever release him from this moment.

Had Rose later been afforded burial in a marked grave, it might have served to acknowledge her station in life as mother of Daniel, but, as it was, birth and death passed all but unnoticed in a place that was familiar with both.

Had it not been for the inner searching of one whose eyes sought the corners of his beggared world for some small reflection of his place within it, then the life of this benighted child might have taken an altogether swifter path to its end. Instead, bereft of the familiar touch of love and the comfort of the steady hand of kin, Daniel developed a deep resolve to fashion an independence of view that gradually closed all doors to feeling and expressions of emotion. If life had revealed itself so – he might have justified – then what cause did he have but to do otherwise?

There was nothing remarkable about this foundling house. Its walls were his guardian and the corridors his guide. The crowded hall and dormitory were his family, bed and comfort, and the shimmering panes of glass in the dusty window frames his view on all else. Body and mind had succumbed to the cloistered narrows of human suffering.

The house that held the parish poor served all who passed its doleful door. The sick, the lame, the lost and insane, all came to rest in joyless plight, schooled only in sorrow and remorseless flight from pain too harsh to bear.

It was regiment both in the ceaseless need and shame of all who sought its shelter, as well as in the appearance and manner of its daily routine. Uniformed waifs and strays, like Daniel, obeyed orders to eat, sleep, and attend lessons. Each activity was interspersed with copious prayers for forgiveness of some misdemeanour he had no recollection of committing. Through all this, he learnt quickly not to ask questions, nor expect answers to the rage of injustice resounding within his growing sense of isolation from everything beyond the confines of his internment. The imprint of a regime of austerity, of common plainness – indeed, the suppression of any desire beyond that to succumb to the will of his betters – was implanted upon the frame of his reasoning as firmly as it was implanted upon the grey code of his garb. With the cries of derision in his ears and the welts of scorn across his backside, the stifled mind of a child limped through the years towards adolescence, accustomed to living, but singularly unacquainted with life.

At the age of ten, or thereabouts – it matters not one day or the morrow, for ten years of silent shame is overmuch to bear, and birthdays step lightly by for fear of waking muted sorrow – the formal days of his education were all but abandoned, and he, along with others, was put to work with men from the newly built House of Industry. He was to clear rock and stone from land around the workhouse in preparation for what was explained as, '*the future prosperity of mankind*'. It was to be his '*privilege*' to work for '*the greater good of all*' and '*the glory of the Lord*'. He accepted the change with his usual studied indifference and puzzlement. He understood '*good*': it was ensuring you had enough to eat, enough fine clothes, and enough money in your pocket; for these were the ornaments that separated him and his kind from ever being good. But, as for rest of it, how could he understand? For they were the words that only good people knew, and they sounded hollow in a way that only added to his bewilderment. He had, as yet, no means of becoming good, and therefore to expect him to know of the benefits it would bring was like asking him to say how riding in a fine carriage would be for the glory of the Lord. Instead, it seemed to him that he was being sent away, denied the shelter of familiar corridors, and tossed into another place – hitherto bounded only by a small frame of glass.

*

In the event, he discovered that work had its merits. He was called by his name – the only one he had ever heard – and besides, he wouldn't have known what to do with two. He was spoken to as an individual, instead of a shadow in some grey hall of correction; he was shown what to do, rather than having it explained in a book or on a slate, and words began to have an association with actions and those around him by way of a language he could see. But best of all he could breathe. He could breathe air that was free of the musty smell of fear and the dank odour of yesterday's gruel; he gulped its salty freshness as it ran in from the sea to box his ears and tan his mousy skin. He watched, learnt, and breathed. Belatedly, he had found a sort of freedom, not yet of body, but of mind. Questions still remained silent within him, but in one of those affairs-of-time moments that embed themselves in the bowels of character forever, he had come to an appreciation of study: the study of the ways of others and their unspoken demeanour. He had come to the study of *mankind*.

*

His awakening from childhood was no great loss to him. Indeed, it could be said he had settled into the adult world direct from the womb; it had opened not only the doors of the orphanage, but also the doors of a world in which he would be able to – if not vanish – then at least escape from the unremitting order imposed upon him in the name of '*the greater good of mankind*'. His freedom ripened his mind and then his body so that he grew in stature, as a sapling competing to be tall, flexing at every change in wind and season that he might assert his right to survive in his own ground.

Three, maybe four years passed, and as his shoulders broadened to accommodate the toil of labour he became increasingly assured A certainty of character now replaced the bewilderment of his younger days; gone was the sickness of parentless reproach, the hours of studious searching in his bed at night and the inner wanderings of his mind by day, seeking some explanation for his wilderness. Instead, he now steered his chosen course; the day was his to labour, and the night to sleep with the comfort of his exertions. He had no allegiance except – strangely – to those less able than himself; however, he rarely dwelt upon such matters unless obliged to justify some rare act of charity or hesitation to further his own independence.

There was, though, one such occasion that stood out above others in the unfolding of his character; the beating of the boy Bonner: '... *a frail youth of no aptitude or intent other than slothfulness ...*' a simple-minded child without thought or manner offensive, '... *was in need of regular and firm correction ...*' who was struck hard and long for no good reason, '... *when, without cause ...*' until, without thought of the consequence, '... *the boy Douglas placed himself squarely and forcibly ...*' he had stood between authority and oppression '... *so as to unwarrantedly interfere and threaten the personage of Mr Elijah Whittle – dutiful overseer to the day's labours ...*' to protect an innocent from further suffering by the embittered hand of Reproach. The judgement of the master of the workhouse was that both the boys Bonner and Douglas were to be found wanting, '... *and that the boy Douglas, yet to be corrected, requires apprenticeship to a trade becoming his vigour.*' and were to be removed from the workhouse.'

It was a judgement of convenience, a lesson in life. A troublesome event – seemingly not the first of its kind – had been resolved at no cost, for the fees of settlement would be borne by the parish and, presumably, without loss of standing to the institution or Mr Whittle.

*

'This is the boy Douglas we spoke of,' announced the master. 'Step forward, boy – smartly now!' He was propelled by an obsequious hand to within arm's length of a large, whiskered oak of a man. The smell of honest labour, mixed with the aromatic puree of frequent association with exotic goods, clashed with the more orderly air of a study set with heavy furniture and ledgers bulging with meticulous records of institutional ritual.

'He is a quiet boy with a ...'

'How do you do, Douglas?' The booming voice stopped the fussing of the master.

'Your servant, sir,' said Douglas.

'Hah! Well spoken. And I, yours. Obedience must be earned, must it not?' Thankfully, before he could think of a reply, the man turned to the master.

'I have a horse who obeys my command, sir. What I need is a man who commands my respect.' Turning to Douglas, he continued, 'He has a steady eye and a firm jaw. I'll sign your papers, sir, and bid you good day.'

Douglas watched, noting the strong hands and bold flourish of the quill across the parchment. His mark was less ornate, though arguably more legible.

The day he was collected from the workhouse by Mr John Capper, merchant and wagoner to the freemen of Liverpool, was a day he had seen many times before. It was a day in waiting: one he had watched play out through a small frame of glass as he gazed into the world away from the routine and constant regulation of communal penury. He had known nothing else: poverty of circumstance, poverty of justice, and poverty of belonging. Now, he was glad to be free of all association with poverty; he looked forward to his share of *prosperity* and the *glory* he felt sure was his right.

As he climbed up onto the seat beside his new master, the rich waft of rum mixed with pitch and coal dust, bedded in and between the boards of the wagon, wrapped him in a cloak as full and rich in splendour as any liveried coachman wheeling a four-in-hand away from some stately residence. As they drove out of the large iron gates he did not look back. The future, as far as he was concerned, hung somewhere above the roofs and spires of the town laid out before him, and he was determined to make of it what he could.

The Art of Character

WHAT FOLLOWED IN THE years ahead was to
be enrichment of a sort rarely matched by the
wealthier burghers – freemen or not, for he was to
acquire a view of a restless society that was not tainted
by birthright or favour. Dashing splendour and abundant
ornament carried no envy, nor did the more sober and
depressing shades of poverty and drudgery weigh upon
him. His was the view of an innocent, an outsider born
free of custom or allegiance to position in society. He had
no guiding hand nor oracle to turn to; the shuttered years
of his childhood served only to brighten the contrast of
his youth. His passing through the gates of the orphanage
was like being reborn, seeing for the first time a world
previously only glimpsed through a grimy window pane.
Now, though, that world was different. It was real, inviting,
and spinning before him like a whirling carousel at a fair.

The swagger and bustle of finery in the streets was set
against the grandeur of the town's proud buildings standing
aloof from the parade of labour at their feet. The songs of
sailors from the many dockside taverns jousted with the

shouts of market traders and the bellowing of cattle as they were herded to and from the coastal barges; together, they duelled with the peals of church bells and the chiming of the Custom House clock. To his mind, it was as busy and devoid of order as to wipe clear all memory of watch and reproach, and he revelled in its extremes with a boldness that becomes one without care for tomorrow. It was at all times exciting, alive with spectacle and entertainment, for as it seemed to Douglas, there was always some new street, some new scene that would reveal itself to his gaze.

His position as Assistant Wagoner, not only gave him an elevated view of the streets of Liverpool, it also introduced him to a new world of trade and commerce. It seemed that anything could be bought in the few square miles of the town and its sheltered harbours. The docks became his haunt. At the end of the day, or when not engaged in collecting or delivering goods around the town, he would go down to the quay in front of the Custom House. There he would indulge his curiosity in the diversity of life pressing round the groaning bellies of the over-full luggers and Mersey barges waiting to discharge their mysterious cargoes onto dry land.

There was no mystery about the baskets of fish landed on the Goree Causeway, nor was there any shortage of interest when kegs of gunpowder were ferried from the magazines at Liscard to be loaded onto the armed brigantines sailing to Africa and the West Indies to trade their assorted wares in exchange for a cargo of human misery. The voyage of the slave traders was the unspoken currency behind the import of flavoursome foodstuffs for the dining rooms of the rich and genteel. The sugar, coffee, tobacco, and rum that found their way into high society also appeared on the tables of the working classes. The pockets and breeches of the sailors and dockside workers, who eased the pulleys and cargo nets of the Atlantic leviathans to the tune of wind and tide, were as full as sails on the open seas. A favour here, a word there, a manifest trimmed, a tally hurried, all passed as rightful dues for the greater good – if not of mankind – then for the kind of man that Douglas had come to know as his kin: the independently minded working man. He had found a niche in life that fitted his view of it. The streets were his boundaries, perhaps even his classroom, as he learnt his trade from the shopkeepers and warehousemen, but they also provided the means of his escape to his schoolyard – to the quays and docksides where he gleaned so much more: the means by which men without privilege in life artfully wrung the most from the precious cargoes that passed through their hands. It was the most practical of study for a young man seeking his place in life's array.

John Capper, as well, was something of an opportunist, no doubt. A proud self-made man, he was enterprising enough to know a sharp mind when he saw one. Douglas's excursions and the growing trust of the dock workers and officials around the quays, was enough for him to advance his business interests by engaging Douglas as runner to the clerks in the Custom House. Thus, for the first time, he had early access to information relating to shipping movements and cargo manifests. This meant that he was able to position his wagons at the appropriate times and berths to secure engagements for long-distance carriage. Such work was always more profitable than the town deliveries, and consequently, his business grew quickly with regular journeys along the increasing number of turnpikes across the county. In due course, Douglas too was rewarded. He found himself journeying further and further afield: north to Ormskirk and Rufford Hall, where there was much building work being undertaken that required regular supplies of mortar and bars of wrought iron for the local blacksmiths, and west to Prescot, St Hellens, and occasionally to Warrington. In such cases, a heavy load would mean slow progress, and if they were fortunate enough to secure a return cargo, as would often be the case from the glassworks at St Hellens, the days would be long and arduous for both men and horses; especially, in bad weather or when the wagon was 'high-sided' or 'shelved' with boards to increase the load.

Douglas's world had grown again. He did not notice the lowering sun or the stinging rain, all he knew was the freedom of the open road as it ran through his veins like the calling of flight to a migrating bird. Every brow, turn, and ford was a landmark; every coach, wagon, cart or trundle had a story to tell by the nature and manner of its load. Foodstuffs from land and sea jostled with coke and coal as fuel for the hungry towns. In the opposite direction, whole trees from forests threaded their way to the coast to be turned into the hulls and masts of ocean-going ships; in between ran all the necessity and frippery of the lord and his lady, their butler and maid, the parson and doctor, the farmer and factory worker; all wended its separate ways into the contrasting settings of the expectant classes.

It was a world apart, and it had taken hold of him in the grip of wanderlust that moves a man to venture beyond the skyline to seek, if not his fortune, then his place in all about him. The road had become his destiny; it was his morning and night, yesterday and tomorrow, friend and foe, tormentor and comforter; it was his beacon, and it led him north and away, north from the familiar outline that had once beckoned but now failed to hold him, and away from his employer, who had seen something of himself in the restless steel of an impatient soul. He knew when to let go.

Their parting, almost to the day of the fifth anniversary of their meeting, was amicable and conducted in a business-like manner of employer and employee. The settlement of release from his terms of engagement and full payment of notes owing was signed and witnessed in the presence of the clerk to the parish of Liverpool. Thereafter, albeit briefly, they became as equals: free of any obligation to the other but mindful of the courtesies due when each had played his part to the full.

*

As Douglas proudly led his two newly acquired and lightly packed Scotch Bay geldings northwards through the town, the familiar signs and names on the shop fronts seemed to offer their support: John Fairweather – Purveyor of Fine Foods; J. Luck – Fishmonger; William Lightfoot and

Son – Sailmaker, and lastly, on Scotland Road itself, Josiah Freeman – Victualler. The thought of his own freedom to choose his path and pace at his own appointment was both liberating and daunting, but for the moment his focus was on what he knew. The road to Preston was the limit of his knowledge; beyond that he would rely on travellers' tales and local gossip gathered over the months at the frequent delays around the toll-gates. Now the choice of road was his, and occasionally, as on the road to Lancaster, his ponies' as they veered in favour of the narrow pack ways for the last few miles up the coast and into town. Jeth was the born leader, and at times he and Shap often seemed to be the willing followers, but the pace was easy and the ponies seemed used to the quieter lanes.

In some small respect, Lancaster reminded him of Liverpool: busy, but not so industrial; regal with its castle, yes, but not so elegant and certainly not so populous. In manner of trade, it served its community in the same way as Liverpool, its harbour and quays courting coastal and ocean-going ships as well as its fishing vessels. It was, however, much smaller, and Douglas soon found his way across the river to the north, where, for the first time, the misty-grey hills, that had been appearing on his skyline for the last few days, blossomed into the credible mountains of Westmorland and Cumberland. These were the hills that he had been warned would bar his journey to the north of Kirby Kendal – should he choose to go that way. He had also been advised to turn east at Preston for the northern industrial towns, where, as story had it, fortunes were to be made in the new cotton and woollen industries. However, on a whim, he had chosen to decline the suggestion. Choosing the leftmost fork, he headed towards the hills.

No sooner had he settled his bearing then he was to think again, for the broad bay before him with its numerous small vessels and craft dancing upon its tetchy waters was, he was told, the most direct road to his goal if he should care to wait until the morning ebb tide. Further enquiry assured him of the truth of the matter, that coaches regularly crossed this way at low water.

And so it was that at first light the following day, after carefully checking the strapping of his ponies' packsaddles, Douglas found himself amongst a party of three horse-drawn carts, a carrier's wagon stacked high with goods bound for Ulverston, and assorted pedlars' trundles, all gathered on the shore at Hest Bank to cross the expanse of Lancaster Sands. What had been a restless sea the day before, had become a lifeless plain: in all extent, a lone and level place, in which neither land nor sea truly belonged as one gave way to the other at the behest of sun and moon. As the tide ebbed each day to expose the shifting sands, it was a reminder to all in these parts of the variability of nature, and their place at the very edge of its truculent forces.

As they followed the guiding hand of the carter onto the seeping surface, the early morning light greeted their cheery good humour with a display of tinctured gold and white diamond stars rising from the thousand rivulets hurriedly returning to the sea. Almost immediately, the land behind became no more than a dark line as they sank below earthly towers and onto the floors of a waterless sea. Their pale horizon was barely distinguishable. To the left, sea and sky blended into a seamless arc of whey-like mist, neither grey nor milk-white, as each spoiled the other's delight; whilst ahead and to the right the pastel shades of land were sucked ever lower as the party headed further out into the sunken shallows. Time and time again they crossed still-flowing streams, as a band of ancient explorers might venture further and further into the unknown, always seeking that first glimpse of what might be their uncharted destiny. It was as they forded the deepest flow yet that the tone of the morning changed. Man and beast, leader and follower, all sensed the lowering light, the rising vapour and the lessening sight of distant scape.

'Stay close an' mind next in line.' It was the carter who spoke, and as he faded from view, it was he who sounded that first haunting call to follow. The louring mist sucked each of them, one by one, into its clutches so that they appeared as fading spectres drifting through a silver-grey screen of clammy wetness. The silence was broken only by the splash of irregular stride through the flowing ground beneath their feet as the last of the tide sought to separate them from their equilibrium. Occasionally, the muffled sound of the carter's horn would set a new bearing as he led his timid flock through the grey that now hung between sea and sky to dampen the spirit and blur the eye.

The scene – if such it could be described, for no eye could see it – was dreamlike in motion, as though time rested on the shoulders of the tousled cortege to relieve them of the need to gauge their passage by any watch or clock made by man. Each moment was as the last: a colourless procession of man and beast, huddled together against a smothering shroud, hypnotised by the note of a siren's call. No voice was raised against the given course. Now a breath of wind, a change of light, a glance behind to check a sound that brings a chill upon the neck, to speed the pace lest one should be the last; shadows enter and leave, left and right, passing and fading as chimeras of the fearful mind dancing from side to side, beckoning first one way and then the other to follow an unseen path.

And then, without warning, a galleon rears as if from the sands itself, full rigged and scudding fast before a storm to scatter all in its passage. Sea creatures rise to the clang of dancing chains, the whip-crack of snapping stays, and the groaning of ancient timbered ribs giving way to the vice-like grip of a certain watery grave.

'God's truth,' goes up the cry from some poor demented soul about to die.

A spitting serpent leaps and lashes hard across the deck to loose a cargo from its hold and set it wild amidst the ghostly armada.

'Hold fast, else Devil takes us all,' comes a second more reasoned call.

'Too late!' for now the last, as chaos-driven hands aghast resign deliverance and wait.

'Damn this mist,' says one.

'What's happened?' begs another.

As if in answer to the final plea, a fearful wail of unseen beast leads all on foot and bended knee to make their peace – alone. As they enter, so they shall depart without goods and chattels or wealth in any part to ease their way. This road that never was had come to life to claim its toll on those who chose its path in lieu of what they knew to be – that sea is not the home of man, nor sand the same as trusty land.

*

The scene is done. No sound or solid account is left. All that remains is the innocent blush of light on sculptured sands. What took place in those few moments is known solely to those who were there, and, should they care to tell their story – it was no hand of Nature that hung over the small party that morning; no other saw the mist, and some have sworn the day was clear and bright throughout, and of course no trace was left in the watery plain.

As the wailing died away, so did the freshening breeze release them from their sodden wrap to gaze upon such a sight as none could countenance as belonging to their world. The scattered forms and familiar shapes of everyday possessions were as flotsam set in grey-black mud amidst the bales and casks of commerce spilled from a wagon resting end-on in the quagmire, pointing skywards, shaft up, dripping straps and broken traces from a crosspiece, where moments before, two strong horses had been hitched, secure. Other carts and trundles were similarly stirred, but of their horses and ponies, there were but two in hand, with three or four more distant, separated from them by a glass-like glaze: miniature decorations on an otherwise landless horizon.

Slowly, the dishevelled figures straightened and hardened into the outlines of souls released from the sorcerer's spell. The bleakness of their manner amidst the wreckage of their livelihood was caught in the rolling eyes and straining leads of the two remaining horses. Leave they must, and soon, for as all knew, the tide would change and reclaim this waste as its own before long. But, which way to go? One by one they turned towards the carter, as though each, in turn, had come to a single mind.

The carter had already absorbed both the mood and appetite of his charges, as well as the lie of their position in the bay. The sun was his timepiece and the rivulets of seawater his compass, but it was the soles of his feet that he trusted more than anything else to steer him clear of the treacherous, shifting sands that would swallow all that remained when the tide returned.

They had strayed in the mist, or the sands had covered the route, as they did on occasion; but he knew, too, that to try and recover the wagon and anything other than the handcarts and trundles would be futile. They were already breaking through the fragile crust; they had to leave.

'Gather in. Come quick. Are all present?' A quick tally told him they were. 'We leave straight'way. What can't be raised, stays.' He hesitated before adding, 'The horses will make their way – others have.'

Douglas hoped he was right. Shap's reins had frayed and he had feared the worst as he had struggled to retain hold of Jeth. He had had no chance to assess his loss, and like the others, he once more stepped into line without question.

*

Two hours later, the feel of dry land under his feet was like the comfort of returning to his own room after a day's labour on the wagon. The casual greeting of the few villagers on the shore soon turned to quite a throng as word of the occurrence spread. Fisherman about to set their nets gathered to listen and pass judgement in equal measure, but of greater importance to Douglas was the information that the tide and current would drive the horses northwards up the coast towards the village of Lindale. After securing grazing for Jeth and buying extra provisions enough for two days travel, he spent an uneasy night reliving the day's curious turn of events.

For the next three days, Douglas traced and retraced the miles of coast and estuary, stopping only to ask for local knowledge and news of any sighting of Shap. All agreed that most horses lost on the sands eventually return, but the question of recovery was a different matter. People were isolated in these parts and looked to the sea for much of their needs; the retrieval of booty, in whatever form, was deemed acceptable so long as ownership was not known. They were careful too, he was told; what was found would often be hidden for months until the authorities – or strangers – had moved on and memories had faded.

This was a bad time. The realisation that more had been taken from him than mere possessions was a shock. The few belongings he had, mattered little to him when counted, but the ponies were his future, and whatever had driven him to secure two, when he had at first thought one to be enough, was now there again to question his judgement.

The unseen presence within us all that guides our favour of left or right, or as a whim turns our glance this way or that to spy a more appealing route, had revealed its hand. With all the impetuosity of a squall on an autumn's day he had been lifted and stirred to face a new direction, without, it would seem, any exertion on his part; all the moments that leave their mark unnoticed had come to lie afresh, to reveal the full impact of his loss upon his desire to make his own way in life. There had been no plan when he left Liverpool, no expectation and no real destination in mind, other than to see for himself what lay beyond his horizon; but in all that he had experienced, from his very first silent plea to be noticed to the enviable study from the quayside of those who sailed to far-off lands, he had a thirst to live by his own rules. The ponies were not only his transport, but they were also to be the means by which he would earn a living as a packman, or perhaps, like John Capper, as a carrier with his own wagon and business. All this had come to him in the same moment as it had been taken from him. Like the villagers and the self-serving community he now walked amongst, he had become hardened by the sleight of hand that gives and takes in unequal measure according to the wiles of wind and tide.

With words of false hope ringing in his ears, he left a drab and darkened place, squeezed as it was between the grey sea and black fells. Quite deliberately he left at dusk when all should be in their homes, and quite deliberately when he passed by any darkened door, he called out loud and clear the name of his lost pony, lest any might not recall his cause or remember his enquiry. He wanted more, he wanted to hammer on the doors and curse their hovels, but he didn't; he left them to themselves: suspicious, wary of outsiders and scavenging on scraps of misfortune. This beggared and mutant coast offered nothing; he left it as one would leave a deep sorrow, buried beneath a rage of anger and injustice, injected as it were into his life-marrow to grow into his very being as a constant reminder of loss.

*

So, I had been carried thus far in my understanding of the man. Douglas's journey was as another's clothes: the same in outward appearance to many, but the folds and bearing were unique to the wearer and distinguished him from all other. However, there is one last testimony which must now be told.

*

Douglas's road north led him deeper into the hills as though to draw him completely under their power. His route was channelled into their shadow and so governed by their presence that the passage of the day was never his own. The way alongside Winander Mere was narrow and awkwardly wandered through oak and larch forests, with only an occasional glimpse of sky in the infrequent passages through open ground. The few dwellings he passed seemed unoccupied, and the only settlement of note was the small hamlet of Bowness, but as the milestone indicated only eight miles to Kirby Kendal he chose to pass it by in favour of another night by the road.

It was not long after, between the hours of fading light and full darkness, that he was aroused by the sure sound of someone in pain. He rose and moved slowly towards the groans, which by now he determined were coming from the direction of the road. He watched from behind a tree as the figure of a large man slumped over a horse rolled unsteadily into view. The groans were interspersed with mutterings and what seemed like sobbing; he was about to turn away, from what was, plainly, a drunken sot relying on the good sense of his horse to see him home, when his foot slipped and he darted into the road in front of the unsuspecting animal. Not unnaturally, it reared up, beaching its blubbering flounder of a load squarely on its back flapping uncontrollably on the uneven surface. The horse, now free of its burden, bolted back the way it had come, and had it not been for the unmistakeable shell-like sound of soft gold and silver coins falling onto stone, Douglas too was of a mind to retreat, for the circumference of the man was more than he could have embraced, and his curses would, clearly, not have given way to reason. For a moment, both he and the man froze in their gradually dawning common assent of the muted call of this ebbing fortune, before they fell as one upon the unseen source of the riches.

To find yourself alone at night lying on hard ground is one thing, but it is quite another to hear the sound of your fortune trickling from your pockets; to then be confronted with the dark image of another's presence along with probing fingers is altogether too much, and so it was for gentleman farmer John Rainscombe that night. With a yelp of surprise and a scream of anguish that cleared a dull head and mind in equal measure, he regained his composure enough to believe he was being robbed and accosted within sight of his front door.

Douglas, too, was shaken by the speed and turn of events. Uncertain as to the outcome, or indeed the manner of occurrence, he turned to regain the cover of the wood. His one thought was to flee with his pony from what had been the most disconcerting few moments of crazed behaviour and circumstance he could ever imagine. As he ran he heard the crack of a pistol shot, and as it faded he could hear the diminishing cries of a drunkard's pleas for assistance to come to his rescue.

That night he and Jeth ran as they had never run before: across common, waste, vale and mountain, away from the uncertainty of a moment's intent and the certainty of its unfolding in the clear head and light of a gentleman's tomorrow.

A Simple Gesture

IT WAS DUSK AND bitterly cold as Douglas approached Freeland. There was no sign of light coming from the house; he shivered as each step drew him closer to the awful moment when he would break a mother's heart. He knocked on the door. He never knocked, nobody did – it was always unlocked. He lifted the latch and leant on the gnarled oak to reveal the glow of a fire and warmth of a Sunday afternoon's baking. He had forgotten it was Sunday.

'Hello ... Mrs Newsome?' He felt like an intruder.

'Come in, Douglas; quickly, close the door.' Christian's mother appeared from the shadow of the stairs, wiping her hands on her apron as she approached him. 'I heard you coming, or rather the geese did.' She smiled. 'Where's Christian?'

His heart stopped – the innocence of the question broke him; he had not even begun to imagine this moment.

'He's dead.' The stark words left him involuntarily. 'He's dead.' He heard himself whisper it again, foolishly, as if once were not enough.

He watched the smile of greeting melt in the slow-burning horror of his words. She raised one hand to her mouth, suppressing a gasp as she stood transfixed: crucified in life, drained by the brutality of his delivery. He felt her eyes scream into his flesh, beseeching him to take back those words; her pain thudded into his chest, tearing at his heart, leeching his lifeblood.

He had no comfort to offer. He had never known such a loss of feeling.

As he watched her start to shiver and then shake uncontrollably, he heard the distant wail of a mother's soul well up from a place far beyond his reach, her breath wrung from her strangled body.

She shrank before his gaze.

Involuntarily, he found himself drawing her small and frail frame into the reaches of his own convulsing body.

How long they remained entwined in their grief he did not know, but it was she who broke the silence.

'Douglas ... tell me this isn't so ... tell me ... tell me,' and then knowing it was, '... tell me what's happened.'

*

As they sat by the fire he told his story. In bouts of unburdening affection, he ranged from the smallest detail of character to the broadest account of their friendship. She, occasionally rocking back and forth in her old hoop-backed chair, as some poignant image or phrase became too much to bear, listened without sign of hearing. He, now and then stopping at the sight of her distress in the hope that the burning silence would in some way cauterise what he knew could not be healed, talked unconditionally to a mother. And then, a look, a question, a slight motion of a helpless hand and he would continue. He omitted nothing, not even his sense that Christian had foreseen the outcome, and then at the last, when he had known the loss of his friend, he spoke of how, even in his exhaustion, he felt Christian's warmth and generosity of spirit embrace him.

As for his own part in the day's events, he was particularly harsh. His guilt required it of him. It was his suggestion to try again after previous attempts had failed; it was his insistence they go on when all looked to be against them; it was his decision to climb the last leg without an anchor when neither of them had tried this approach before. In his heart he had known the danger, but once he had reached the top he had been sure he would be able to protect his friend. He had not accounted for the rope breaking as it did.

He looked up from his confession. Her eyes were closed but her words were clear: 'It was just a rope of straw, a golden rope of straw … that's all …'

He covered her sleeping form with the coarse woollen blanket that had fallen from her lap, and after putting more logs on the fire he returned to the stool to watch the growing flames curl and wrap their warmth around her soul.

He felt no such respite from the day's sufferings; but in the quietest hour there must have been some small grace from torment, for on awakening he was clear in his course and resolved as to the manner of its execution. The house door was already open and perfectly framed Mary's silhouette; she stood outside with her back to him, gazing up into the softening pearl whites and greys of dawn. He stated his intention in the hushed roughness of voice that betrayed the nearness of his slumber. It was not his way to seek approval, neither did he wish to disturb her thoughts, but as he passed her motionless figure, a stray glance betrayed his hope.

She touched him lightly on the arm: 'Thank you…I'll send others to follow.'

*

He made his way back onto the fells. The simplicity of his resolve checked the horrors of his mind. Comfort, if comfort it was, now accompanied him on his quest to recover his friend's body.

He retraced their route to the point where they had struck off to gain height across the snowfield. On this occasion that was not his objective; instead, he continued along the valley bottom until he judged he would be somewhere close to where his friend must lie. He looked up; the walls of rock and ice stared back. He was standing in a graveyard, nature's garden of boulders: tombstones tossed from the mountains in lasting memorial. His bones ached with the enormity of the task before him.

Douglas had never fully appreciated the sense of peace that Christian had found in these hills. His own view was that they were there … just there; obstructions to be overcome, challenges maybe, but ultimately they were just there by some whim of nature. But now as he started to quarter the ground and constrain his view to that which was close to him, he began to notice the harsh elegance of line and the subtle contrast of tone and detail of form. The intrusion of his search in part destroyed what he observed so that he could easily see the effect of his presence in the snow, but even such a simple awareness was new to him, and slowly he began to sense the scale of the place and his impact upon it.

After some time and without any real feeling of hope, he stopped. Continuing like this, he thought, as though he would find his friend like some stray vessel in a white ocean, now seemed to have little prospect of success. If this land was going to release Christian it would require more from him.

He stood and listened. For the first time in his life, he just listened. He listened so hard that sight was lost, he became becalmed in his body; he listened for so long that sound slowed until time withdrew. Now, instead of the emptiness of silence, he found another influence: a weight bearing down upon his shoulders that required his attention before releasing him to move within its sphere. He noticed the light sigh of breath as it teased his lungs before escaping to become a part of the greater heaviness. He became aware of a faint harmony, as each breath – unnoticed, caught the passing breeze to join a flow over and around each obstacle, filling every crevice – unseen, before restlessly moving on to the next. All the time, in the background, the accompaniment: the cello to the violin, the bass to the tenor, the stern undercurrent of the surrounding rock as it drew all free air towards its heights, and then something else: the whisper – the contrapuntal arpeggio that should not have been there, displacing all others in its awkwardness. It came as a kiss in the dark on his cheek to startle, not as a continuous flow of air, but more of a broken chord from an uneasy score of memories. He inclined his head in its direction and waited. The stillness returned, and as he drifted back along the sequence of resonating notes he felt the nature of the path he was seeking as much as he would the touch of a hand on his shoulder. He had been looking for the body of his friend, whereas, he should have been seeking his presence.

As long as this land stood, Christian and whatever had happened in the gully would be a part of it; it would be etched into the character and aura of this place. He had listened and had heard and it was on these terms that he would be guided to what he sought.

He had made a discovery, albeit, with a little help, he had experienced something unusual to which he would return to in the near future. He had been introduced to the ever-present and telltale sounds of the past as it played its accompaniment to the rhythms of the present.

He followed the wisp of wind as it danced from boulder to boulder flicking tails of snow into the air like tiny silver curls lost in the wake of a passing angel. He moved away from the valley floor and onto the lower reaches of a steeper gradient. There lay the lightly dusted shroud that now concealed his friend's corpse. How he wished for anything other than this to have been his quest. He stood still, numb, waiting for it to fade, to melt away, to rise again, to speak … but no, it was real. Everything was as it was, because … because of him. He knelt and finally, gently, touched reality.

He raised the stiff body onto his shoulders. He turned to retrace his steps. A shout from below alerted him to three small figures about to make their way up the slope; he signalled for them to wait. He and Christian had started together and they should finish together. It was the least he could do before moving on.

*

For Christian's mother, the weeks and months that followed were joyless and full of long dark hours that etched deeply into her countenance. As custom would have it, she was rarely seen outside of her home, but those who called were all too aware of her plight. Farmer Bowes had been one of the first to express his condolences, and all agreed that his settlement of wages and defrayment of the customary heriot was both generous and kind. The few cattle and sheep belonging to the family were to be sold, thus providing enough money for her immediate needs, but the outbuildings were to remain as shelter for the farmer's stock as he or his stewards required. Likewise, it was agreed that the horses would continue to be made available to the farmer and he would make provision for their upkeep at Freeland in return. In all, everything that could be done to relieve her of practical concerns was done, but no amount of kindness could lessen her grief. This most natural of sorrows would not yield to any mortal reparation; it was as if, overnight, she had been shorn of the last vestige of her identity as a mother, and would slowly succumb to be seen as someone who would fade from the social fabric of purposeful occupation.

It was from within this confused cloak of despair and need hanging over Freeland that Douglas slowly emerged as a figure of strength. The same stubborn, combative turn of mind that resisted convention and censure was now the rock that Mary clung to. It was his presence that did not fade; it was he who took it upon himself to call on a regular basis to fetch and carry for her, and when not attending to daily necessities, it was he who comforted her. Such as he was able to do was not fully known to him, but there was mutual recognition of shared melancholy that set aside the constraints on the more honest revelations of the heart.

In other circumstances, such callings would not have been without disapprobation, by some at least, as Douglas's part in this whole affair was not yet settled in the minds of all. But, as he had long been considered as someone outside of social pretension, the value of disdain was, for him, muted. It was, though, not so for Mary; she bore the burden for them both until during one of their many close and earnest discussions she, unwittingly, took up the torch on the next leg of this entangled journey.

'If I could just *see* something of what he …' Her voice faded as it always did when trying to express what it was she really wanted. She tried again: '… something of what he … he *felt* in those mountains … does that sound foolish, Douglas?'

It didn't; of course, it didn't. But how could he explain such feelings, such emotional belonging to someone who had never been there?

'I could take you…' The words were out of his mouth before he realised what he was saying. 'I mean …'

It was too late; the light in her face told him he would be returning to inescapable demons once more.

During the next few days she seemed buoyed by the anticipation of once again sharing a part of her son's life; even Douglas, now acknowledged as the source of the idea, began to see it as an opportunity of reaching a conclusion to his own part.

*

It was on Easter Monday, April 1801, that Douglas, Mary, and a few close neighbours, set off from Freeland to retrace her son's final footsteps. The day was bright and there was a sparkle to the air that mirrored her expression. A wistful looking pony had been bridled for her use, but, to begin with, she chose to walk and enjoy the close presence of those around her. It had been three clear months since she had been anywhere other than to chapel, and she found it refreshing to engage once more in the hushed company of neighbourly confidences.

To her surprise, what started as a personal pilgrimage in search of solace and understanding, gradually turned into a community outpouring of wholehearted support –

with maybe just a little curiosity. At every turn and brow in the road, it seemed that more and more people waited to join the procession as it wound its way towards its unspoken destination. Men, women, and children dressed in their Easter finery tripped onto the fells like some pageant first-stepping into spring. To begin with, Douglas was concerned at the seeming gaiety of the assembly, but as Mary pointed out, it was not her intention to weep amid all this goodwill, and besides most would no doubt drift away as the going became steeper.

For a while, this unusual alliance of frivolity and solemnity continued its way to its uncertain goal and purpose. The slim girls, in their colourful frocks and country bonnets, flitting back and forth between bustling ladies in their layered dresses and fashionably stiffened hats with wide flouncing brims, contrasted – as they giggled and wiggled their way across the greening fellsides like an early onset of spring – with the more steady step, staid breeches and waisted jackets of the men, and Mary's more sombre attire.

In due course, Mary was to be proven right; youngsters did find other amusements amongst the playground of stone and water. All but a few of the women also retreated, as those remaining left what once passed for use as a miner's track to make their way towards the broad mouth of the valley. In the end there remained the best part of a score, in roughly equal numbers of men and women, with the women taking turn and turnabout on the two additional horses that had been hurriedly pressed into service as numbers had grown.

As the gaiety subsided behind them, the women's conversation turned easily to reminiscences of the Newsome family's arrival in the valley, the improvements they made to Freeland, and Christian's likeness, in so many ways, to his father. It was comforting to Mary to hear the respect with which they spoke of Christian's good nature and willingness to help others. His love and care of horses and his ability to work them in tandem had been much admired. Mary knew this as she knew herself, but it was warm and pleasing to hear it spoken of so freely.

The men were less ready to bridge the years that divided the venturesome excursions of youth from the servitude and duties of the older working man. Douglas felt their unease in his presence as some unspoken accusation or reprimand for a self-evident truth; it was, if nothing else, he told himself, an inevitable consequence and something he would have to add to his lot.

Nevertheless, as the party drew together, it was Douglas who took the opportunity to relive some haunting memories. He pointed out the rocks and buttresses that he and Christian had first scrambled over in their bid to uncover the mysteries behind every ragged brow and angled corner. He said nothing about the escape or sense of freedom, the feeling of detachment or aloofness from convention they felt, nor did he offer any comment on the quickening of the pulse or the sharpness of mind that comes before the next uncertain hold or narrow step. All this was his to hold onto.

The mood changed as the collective ear of the group now quietly absorbed the sincerity of his impromptu reminiscences. For most, this was the furthest they had ventured into the hills and as the desolate stillness – so often encountered in these sheltered corridors – wrapped itself around the intrusive throng, some small appreciation of the insignificance of their presence seeped into the common mood.

As they huddled together at the foot of the glories about them, Douglas lowered his voice to catch the moment. 'I have no …' he tried again. 'It is not easy for me to say what I feel, but … if it were ever possible that two souls of liberty could share … could come together as one … then, it was Christian who showed me these hills. Without his eyes I would not have seen such beauty; without his words, I would not have heard such truths, and …' he turned to Mary, 'without his friendship, I would have known neither.'

The silence about them deepened to an aching vacuum that bound them all the tighter for their want of understanding.

'Before I knew of your wishes to come here,' he said quietly, 'I marked a place that I know Christian found to be of great beauty and held in strong favour as all that he thought so dear about this land. It is not far from here, but we can go no further from it without undue discomfort. If you wish …'

Mary raised her hand imperceptibly. 'Please, lead us to this place.'

With the merest nod of agreement, Douglas moved off towards the low rise that marked the boundary between what would be told and what would remain unsaid. Freed from their own ties, the others followed – grateful to be released from their unease but now eager not to be left too far behind.

As promised, their destination was soon reached. Leaving their horses, they followed Douglas carefully up the natural line of the steep approach to a low, rocky knoll. Each took their place on the small, galleried plateau so that the force of grandeur bore down upon them. Ahead lay the full round of the brooding valley heights; bronzed with the pale light from the reflected sun – its upper walls having not yet shed their winter crown. The tearful whites of the gullies, so deeply etched into the higher reaches, faded to the greys of the more sheltered lower contours; all of this was set within the proud, rugged outlines of the ever-watchful ranks of buttresses pressing down upon them.

It was Mary who broke the spell, 'It's beautiful … so … so … strong.'

It was she who first noticed the red-brown flame of colour as the sun glanced off the face of a forged iron staff, resting at a slight angle from the vertical against the mottled grey of a recently cleaved slab of rock. She moved closer. She had seen the likeness before and knew it as that which Christian had carried on his trips into the hills with Douglas. It was entwined with two or three coils of rope and set as though it had just been left there, waiting to be taken up and used in some further adventure.

She bent down; her palms cradled just above its head.

'And this is your work, Douglas?' she whispered without lifting her gaze.

'If you think it inappropriate, it is but lightly fixed and

would take but a moment to remove – just say; I should have asked …'

She gently raised one hand in that characteristically tender gesture that told him all was – in the circumstances – just as she would have wished.

*

The journey back was an altogether more congenial affair. The sense of unease had faded, and Mary's pleasure with Douglas's unexpected gesture had been made clear when she spoke of her wish to return – in his company – as she might now and then desire. In truth, she did command her intention to him – though softly – and as he pledged himself to her service, so did he feel Destiny's hand bind him ever tighter to this land and its callings to his spirit.

Understanding

ALL I HAVE IS behind a door into darkness. The roar of fire and peal of the Devil's anvil cannot deaden what cannot be touched. The more I beat the lifeless iron, the more I hear the fading screams. Each hammer blow must strike out every last modicum of self-pity left in me, lest I should seek to deny my part in this sorrow. The twisted, ugly, reddened, spitting bar may yet yield and turn into something new, but the same cannot be said for my soul.

*

It is nearly ten years since I wrote those words. I still have the scrap of paper folded in between the pages of a letter from Mary telling me not to torment myself so, for she placed no blame upon my shoulders for what had happened. She spoke kindly of my efforts to mark a place to which she could return whenever she felt the need. It was in this letter that she quoted a passage from the Cumberland Pacquet's review of Mr Bacon's writings:

" … It is more pleasing to have a lively work, upon a sad and solemn ground, than to have a dark and melancholy work, upon a lightsome ground; judge therefore the pleasure of the heart by the pleasure of the eye."

Those words are now embroidered on cushion covers that she keeps close by when sitting in the evening. She says their touch brings fond memories and allows her to rest in the past knowing that Christian's love of the hills is still remembered for him. Like her, I too rely on touch; her letter still brings me hope. Adversity is not without its comforts and desires. I often read the faded words and draw upon her learning and strength to seek release from my own self-reproach. In return, I have the pleasure that something of the bond I shared with Christian was given back to her. Of course, in those days we went often to the mountains to visit that place so dear to Christian; sometimes we were alone and at times others came too, but always there was an energy that seemed to feed our conversation and aid our search for understanding. I was as driven as Mary to grasp the sense of what had happened. It was as though our lives mirrored the other: she looking for love lost and I seeking love I had never known. We were locked together in a quest for answers.

She had a way of drawing words from me that I didn't know were there; hidings that had never seen daylight were aired and placed in order, as though some natural science had sooner known what we did not.

I remember she kept a journal. She would read her writings and ask what I thought. Much of it was beyond my education, but when she spoke, I knew the truth of what was said. Her life had been hard too. The loss of her mother at birth, stirred something inside me that had long been kept silent. I could not speak when she told me. Until then, I had not seen fit to tell anyone my story, but in the days after, my outpouring was as an unloosening from a knot tied tight within me. I began to feel free from the years of reproach and judgement, and released from the burden of an overlong kept secret. In the midst of all else, I came to accept the generosity of spirit that had been cast loose within me.

Such stirrings are not lightly admitted, but with Mary's guidance I came to see the part played by the past in the present: each moment is an occasion of choice, an opportunity to do or not – to take or to give, to hold or to let go, to stay or to leave; each chosen way becomes the foundation stone for the next, and so on until the last. My mother's final act was to give of herself, knowing that as she did she would fail in her duty as a mother. Instead of being abandoned, I now saw my whole life as leading to this moment. If I could in some way fulfil the duty of a son to Mary, then at least I might heal a sore that had begun the day I was born. It was as if I had carried an injustice and passed it in turn to Mary. If I had chosen to walk away, then who knows where it would have struck next. I had a chance to put right a wrong, balance an injustice, and bring peace to a mother. I decided to stay.

*

Those long days and months after Christian's death was

time spent searching for a new road. Neither of us had any sense of a future, we could not see beyond unvarying darkness that hid all accepted patterns of daily life. Forging, growing, cutting, milking, carrying, were done half as should be or not at all. In each labour was an unseen weight, a lost cause, a forgotten motive, a jaded will. Life had no meaning and time no place. Reasoning became our shelter and sorrow our knowledge. As we mourned, so did we grow in our understanding that life, or death, is not all, for there is much that lingers to trouble and much that stays to console. What is lost remains and, in some way, renews those who seek to dwell within such memories.

It is life that is fallible: a kingdom that rules by might alone to parade its strength in the absence of reason – other than to survive, will eventually become lost in its own inscrutability. Time will be its only measure. As each life ends and each empire falls to crumple in the sands of its temples to short-lived ideals, so the influence of wonder will wane. The power of the physical mind will grow in everything but humility. Conceived notions of reality will be based upon incomplete perceptions of the whole body of being. Life will become proud and vain in the glory of its achievements to the exclusion of all other.

Mary's Peace

*

Now, statues solemnly stand in exclamation of wonder of some ancient craft that honed a stone into a man, to then gaze forth to proclaim the might of hand above that which, under some impassioned law, first guided life from beyond the shores and sands of time, to wait in vain, with frown and furrowed brow, for what had come from boundless stores, to understand that life was ever more than could be carved from earth, spun by wind, cast from fire or turned by water.

Now, who is there to tell a man what it is that shall come after him when his time is done?

*

Settlement of Mind

MANY YEARS HAVE PASSED since Christian's death. How many I no longer know; suffice to say the passing of time troubles me no more.

Douglas has stayed true to his word, attending to my every want and filling that space within me as long as I have need. Above all else, though, I know I will remain surrounded by his presence and nature. It is as though in one there is the charity of my dear son, and in the other an inner calm that offers comfort from the silence of a mind long last at rest.

I have no words to say what it is that takes another in hand to tell that Death does not demolish all, save, it is enough to know that mysterious quality that comes to unite all as one in a porcelain union of many. It is, perhaps, in humankind the inner intellect: that unseen microscopic pore that besets all body-parts with inward fire to drive its course; chance be, it is that unspoken sense that evades our knowing to labour without acclaim, or, possibly, is it the quietly spoken voice that errs upon the side of caution to arrest an unthought notion?

If any such is true, then we are as yet but half of what we know and less still of what could be. What is certain is that no part of man can claim right over this knowing, for no man has yet created other than that which reflects his own likeness. What is made comes from what is already given, and not from the store of humankind.

If not of life, this mysterious part, then what else can lay claim? Of earth, air, flame, or water there is no doubt that each too takes its turn, but as to knowing its place, that surely is inconceivable. Life came from some store not of its making, this much is plain. Therefore, what is in life was itself already there in waiting: some exalted part from something more than itself, the essence of being perhaps? In which case, such essence is in all else too, still waiting for recognition and knowing.

It is these truths I have come to: the truth in the desert is the only truth. The water that falls is clear; its source is pure and sweet. In the ways of the world, the desert is defiled. The water is polluted and becomes sour.

*

It is from the ground of such emptiness of understanding that lays bare all conscious thought that I came to attend this matter. It is though the shedding of tears opened a door to the soul and I passed through alone. Something I knew to be there had been revealed as though patiently awaiting my attendance, and yet I had no means with which to tell of its being.

But now all that has changed. Douglas and I have had

many conversations. We have spoken long and earnestly, and when the need arises we have stood and listened as night falls on that special place in the valley. I have watched the ways of others and heard scores of arguments for and against the superiority of one person's view over another's. In all matters of science, physics, theology, and natural philosophy it seems that no account is given of the first, or can be given of the last. There is no doubt of the capacity of the mind to conceive of explanations for many things that engage its powers; but for it to acquire knowledge of that greater compass of being, whilst remaining in the shattered dreams of its desire, is beyond all mortal comprehension. To be the object of the downfall of so much, and then to seek knowledge of its presence and meaning, is to confuse reality with the fullness of all possibilities, and reason with the completeness of all understanding. It is to confuse life with being and the role of one with the other.

At some point in life there comes the dawn that it is more than just a shell on the shore of tomorrow, driven by the wind and tide of eternity to make what it will of its place amongst all else. It is not until we step outside of this fragile mask that we see our finished being and realise the worth of our part in the time-full world. It is not as a shell, or even as a shore full of shells, that life is cast: it is instead as an unfinished sculpture that awaits discovery and thereby the wherewithal to fulfil its potential. The object, the place, and the reason are all mere distractions to what is offered. It is the means and the path we seek; the outcome awaits our presence.

I, myself, have become both the matter and means by

which this transition will come to pass. I am the book, the page and the word; the writer, reader, teacher and student. I am the full embodiment of being: the inner quiet, the child at rest, the mortal and immortal expression of existence that lives to draw upon the fullness of two worlds to declare the unity of both as the goal.

And so, I have come to my peace: a settlement of mind at last, and an end to doubt about my part and worth in the glorious firmament above.

*

Mary E. Newsome
Newlands 1828